Benjamin Britten

ALBERT HERRING

Op 39

A comic opera in three acts

Libretto by Eric Crozier,
freely adapted from a story of Guy de Maupassant

Vocal Score by Henry Boys

BOOSEY & HAWKES

Boosey & Hawkes Music Publishers Ltd
www.boosey.com

Published by Boosey & Hawkes Music Publishers Ltd
Aldwych House
71–91 Aldwych
London
WC2B 4HN

www.boosey.com

AN IMAGEM COMPANY

ISMN 979-0-060-01386-7

Reprinted with corrections 2008
This impression 2014

Printed in England by The Halstan Printing Group, Amersham, Bucks

Cover design by John Piper

Dedicated to

E. M. FORSTER

in admiration

CONTENTS

Characters vi
Cast of the first performance vii
Instrumentation viii

ALBERT HERRING

Act I

Scene 1 The morning room in Lady Billows' house, Loxford 1
Interlude 91
Scene 2 Mrs Herring's greengrocery shop 100

Act II

Scene 1 Interior of a small marquee set up in the vicarage garden 162
Scene 2 Mrs Herring's greengrocery shop 247

Act III

Scene Mrs Herring's greengrocery shop 281
Threnody 318

CHARACTERS

Lady Billows, *an elderly autocrat*	Soprano
Florence Pike, *her housekeeper*	Contralto
Miss Wordsworth, *head teacher at the Church School*	Soprano
Mr Gedge, *the vicar*	Baritone
Mr Upfold, *the mayor*	Tenor
Superintendent Budd	Bass
Sid, *a butcher's shophand*	Baritone
Albert Herring, *from the greengrocer's*	Tenor
Nancy, *from the bakery*	Mezzo-soprano
Mrs Herring, *Albert's mother*	Mezzo-soprano
Emmie (*village children*)	Soprano
Cis (*village children*)	Soprano
Harry* (*village children*)	Treble

The action of the opera takes place at Loxford, a small market-town in East Suffolk, during April and May of the year 1900.

***Note.** The part of Harry should be sung by a boy with an unbroken voice, who can act well and sing in a natural urchin manner. If his chest notes are not strong enough he can change parts with Emmie in the ensembles, and in other cases sing the alternative notes provided.

Albert Herring was written to launch the first season of the English Opera Group and was first performed at the Glyndebourne Opera House on 20 June 1947. It was later given at the Amsterdam and Scheveningen Music Festival, the Lucerne International Music Festival, and at the Royal Opera House, Covent Garden.

CAST OF THE FIRST PERFORMANCE

Lady Billows .. .. Joan Cross
Florence Pike .. .. Gladys Parr
Miss Wordsworth .. .. Margaret Ritchie
Mr Gedge .. .. William Parsons
Mr Upfold .. .. Roy Ashton
Superintendent Budd .. .. Norman Lumsden
Sid .. .. Frederick Sharp
Albert Herring .. .. Peter Pears
Nancy .. .. Nancy Evans
Mrs Herring .. .. Betsy de la Porte
Emmie .. .. Lesley Duff
Cis .. .. Anne Sharp
Harry .. .. David Spenser

Conductor: Benjamin Britten
Producer: Frederick Ashton
Designer: John Piper
Orchestra of the English Opera Group

INSTRUMENTATION

Flute (doubling Piccolo and Alto Flute)
Oboe
Clarinet (doubling Bass clarinet)
Bassoon
Horn
*Percussion (1)
Harp
String Quartet
Double Bass

* glockenspiel, bells (F, B♭, D), triangle, castanets, whip, block, tambourine, side drum, tenor drum, bass drum, timpani, cymbals, gong

Note. The recitatives are accompanied by a piano played by the conductor.

DURATION

Act I: 53 minutes
Act II: 56 minutes
Act III: 28 minutes

Performance materials available on hire
Study score and libretto on sale

Study score 979-0-060-01385-0
Libretto: English 979-0-060-01388-1
German 979-0-202-51930-1

ALBERT HERRING

Words by
ERIC CROZIER

Music by
BENJAMIN BRITTEN
Op. 39

ACT I

Scene I The morning breakfast room in Lady Billows' house, Loxford.

CURTAIN Florence is hurriedly clearing away breakfast things for one on to a tray.

Quick and heavy
(Allegro e pesante) ♩. = 144

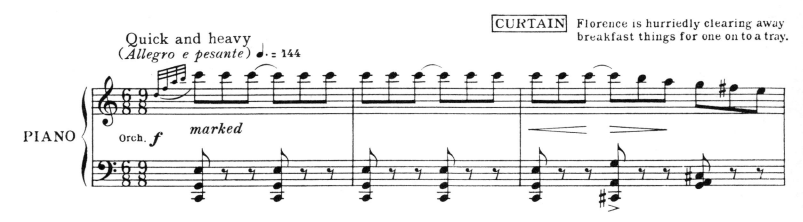

PIANO
Orch. f
marked
express.
She takes the tray out to the kitchen - - - - - - and comes back with a feather duster.
cresc.
ff
marcatiss.

Slow
(Lento)
LADY BILLOWS (off)
Florence stops work and goes upstairs to listen.
Flo - rence!
Fl.
f very marked
sf
Str.
pp sempre
Florence comes back.
(p)
LADY BILLOWS (off)
ff
Tell the mid-wife! – She's not to......!
Quick, as before
(Allegro, come sopra)
She continues dusting and tidying.
FLORENCE
mf
Ve-ry good, mi-la-dy!
Orch. f very marked
express.
dim.

2
Fl.
pp marked
express.
Harp
Str. pizz.
sim.
Str.
pp
Bsn.
marked
express.
Ob.
pp marked
heavy
(pesante)
express.
sim.
Str.
pp
expr.
Hn.
pp cresc.
sempre cresc.
sim.
LADY BILLOWS (off)
Slow
(Lento)
Flo - rence!
3
As at the start
(Come prima)
sffpp
Orch. f marked

Slow
(Lento)
Flo - rence!
FLORENCE
Florence goes upstairs again.
Here, milady!
Slow
(Lento)
Vln.
sfpp
f very marked
sf
Str.
f
sempre pp
p
mf
Florence comes back.
ff
f LADY BILLOWS (off)
Make him tear it up! Make him tear it up!
Dust - bin!
FLORENCE
Yes, milady!
Just on half-past ten!
poco a poco cresc.

4
As at the start
(Come prima)
Florence gets her household book and pencil, and notes her latest instructions.
Orch. f very marked
FLORENCE f Writing - - -
Doc-tor Jes-sop's mid-wife.... must-n't
sfpp
Hn.
Str.
pp but heavy
(ma pesante)
Flo.
touch il-le-gi-ti-mates....
f
5
sempre f
Ad-vert in chemist's window... in-de-cent....
pp marked
Bsn.

Flo.
Tear it up!
Call at
pp
cresc.
pp marked
Clt.
mf
Prim-rose Cot-tage....
Must stop Wil-liam mak-ing such....
mf
rude nois-es or else.....!
Buy a breakfast cup....
Ob. marked
mf pp
cresc.
checking back on earlier notes
6 p cresc. sempre
Load of logs for Number Six, The Mount....
f
Str. pp smooth (legato)

Flo.
Mit - tens for Mis - ter Pil - grim.... Did they count how
pp
Flo.
ma - ny from the alms-house want-ed cop-ies of the Bish-op's ser-mon?....
Flo.
f
No more pop-pies........ in al - tar vas - es.... Looks too Ro - man..
sf p
f
pp
Flo.
più f
Vi - car must warn choir-boys........... Make res-pons - es quick - er....
sfp
f
pp

Florence shuts her book in despair.
7 the same speed
(l'istesso tempo)
sustained, desperate
f (sost. e disperato)
Flo.
One ....
cresc.
W.
ff
Hn.
Harp
Str.
life - time,
One
Timp.
D.B.
brain, One .... pair.......... of hands are
all too few for La - dy

8
with force
(con forza)
Flo.
B. Each day some new i - dea makes
Ob.
ppp
Fl.
ppp
Str.
pizz.
pp
new de - mands......... Up - on her sense of char - i - ty.
Clt.
molto cresc.
molto cresc.
sim.
9
f
One .... life - time,
ff

Flo.
One brain, One........ pair........ of hands Are all too few
ff
f
mf
10
passionate (♩=♩)
(appassionato)
for La - dy B. But
pp express.
pp very sweetly (dolciss.)
oh!.. But oh!.. But oh!...
più cresc.
cresc.

as at the start
(come prima)
Flo.
Sometimes I wish ....
There is knocking at the conservatory door.
f
più cresc.
express. f dim. molto
Florence breaks off and goes to open the door.
11
ff
very marked
(ff very marked)
(ff very marked)
Miss Wordsworth, the Vicar, Superintendent Budd and the Mayor enter.
Recit. (conversational)
MISS WORDSWORTH
I hope...we're not too ear-ly, Flo-rence?
FLORENCE
Oh no, Miss!
ffz

*)Throughout the work the Piano chords should be sustained until the following chord or rest.

Recit.
MAYOR
No, you're slow! Ex - act - ly right by
SUPER
checking it by his watch.
Ten se-conds fast I make that.
Piano
p
Moving to the window - - - - - - - - - - -
MISS WORDSWORTH
Oh! I find it so re-fresh - ing.... to es-cape from school a sun-ny day like
May.
mine.
(Piano)
pp
sim. ad lib.
Miss W.
this.
VICAR
Play - ing tru - ant?
SUPER
shaking his watch
Fun - ny be - ing slow! Ne - ver known it...
mf

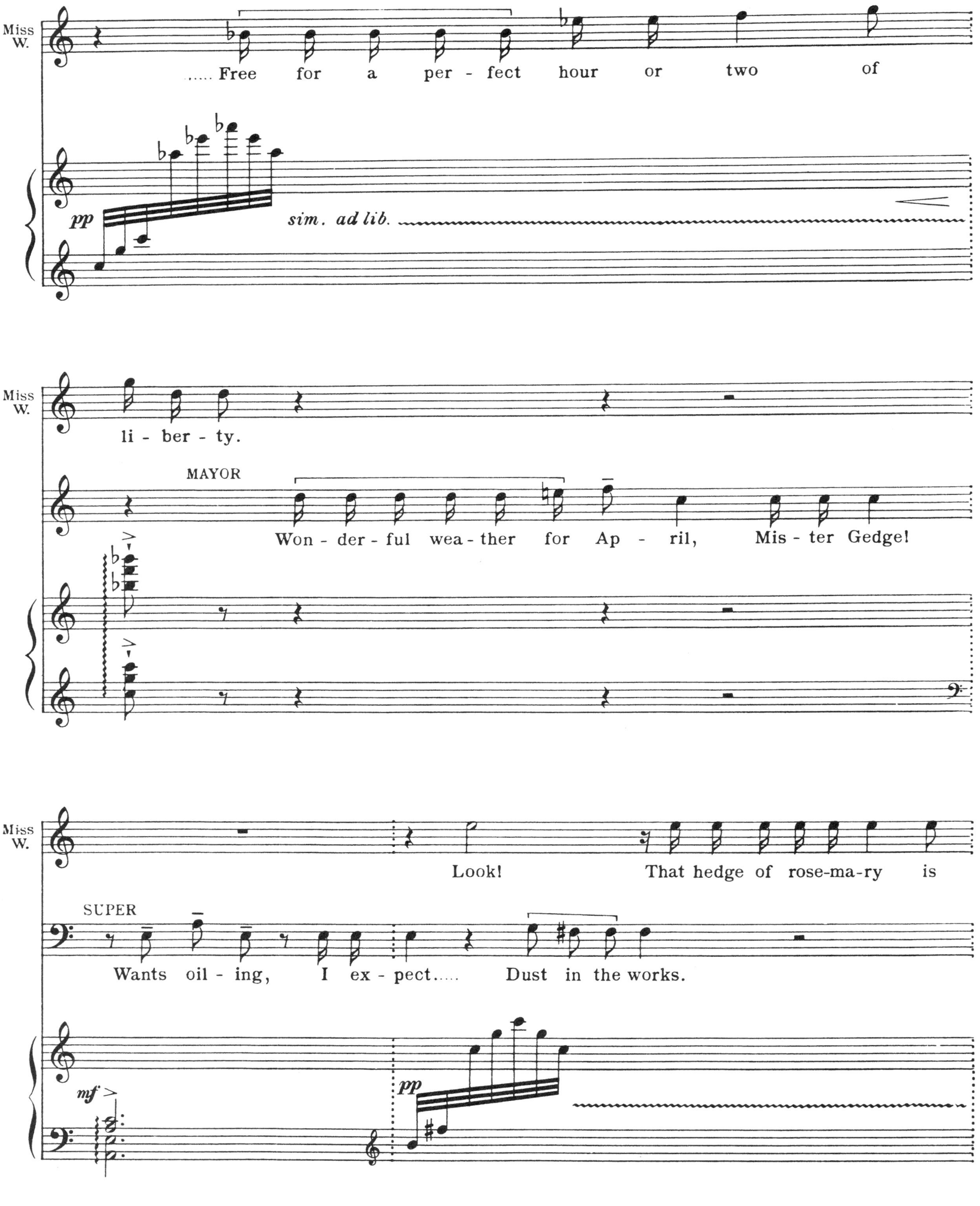
Miss W.
..... Free for a per - fect hour or two of
pp
sim. ad lib.
Miss W.
li - ber - ty.
MAYOR
Won - der - ful wea - ther for Ap - ril, Mis - ter Gedge!
Miss W.
Look! That hedge of rose-ma-ry is
SUPER
Wants oil - ing, I ex - pect..... Dust in the works.
mf
pp

Miss W.
hum-ming with bum-ble-bees!
VICAR
Quite per-fect, Mis-ter Mayor! Pro-mis-es a splendid May and June.
MAYOR
That it does. It was.....
f SUPER
"In like a lion, out like a lamb!"— that was true of March this year!
p solemn
MISS WORDSWORTH
sweetly (dolce)
"And lo! the win-ter is past, the rain is o-ver and gone, The
cresc.
sweetly (dolce) cresc.
VICAR
"The rain is o-ver and gone, The
pp
cresc.

Miss W.
flowers ap - pear on the earth!"
MAYOR impatient
Well, since we're here...
Vic.
p
flowers ap - pear on the earth!"
Sol - o-mon's Song, you know!
ff
more agitated
(più agitato)
rapidly
SUPER
Her La-dy-ship was ve - ry dis - tressed when she heard a - bout Cur - tis - 's
f
MISS WORDSWORTH
f
Ap - pall - ing!
VICAR
f
They tell me that's her third!
Sup.
daugh - ter.
She won't con - fess the fa - ther,

Miss W.
Li - ly Jar - vis is an - oth - er prob - lem!
MAYOR
It's hap - pen - ing far too of - ten!
Sup.
sil - ly girl!
VICAR
Drun - ken fa - ther, mo - ther a slat - tern,—
Sup.
Twins, if you please!
MISS WORDSWORTH
Their poor .... child - ren!...
MAYOR
Some - thing must be
Vic.
these things breed im - mor - al - i - ty in the young.

Miss W.
f
Her
May.
done!
Vic.
f
A firm stand now before the evil
SUPER
f
Hear, hear!
f
Miss W.
La-dy-ship is all for that!
May.
più f
Strong measures are es-sent - ial
Vic.
spreads!
Sup.
f
Tho' she ex - ag-ger-ates oc-cas-ionally!...

Miss W.
May.
Vic.
Sup.
cresc.
Most es - sent - ial!
now!
cresc.
Of course they are! This
cresc.
Hear, hear!
più f
Florence comes in hurriedly.
Oh yes! I have great hopes ...
cresc.
Cer-tain-ly!
ff
Prac-ti-cal mea - sures...
Fes - ti - val i - dea may help! I am all for that! ...
cresc.
Hear, hear! Hear, hear! ...

ritardando
Miss W.
mf
Oh! Her La-dy-ship!
FLORENCE
ff
HUSH! She's here!
May.
f
Careful now!
Vic.
pp
Ah! La-dy Bil-lows!...
Sup.
p
Here she comes!
fff
ritardando
12
Heavy march ♩= 52
(Alla marcia grave)
Lady Billows appears at the top of the stairs and walks heavily and delib-
Harp
Str.
pp marked
Timp.
D.B.(pizz.)
heavy (pesante)
sim.
cresc.
sim.
erately down
sempre più f
W.
sf p
Str.

She crosses unexpectedly to the window and pushes it open
fp
fp
13
LADY BILLOWS
with force
(con forza)
Stuf-fy! To-bacco stink! Nasty
cresc.
f
6
pp
poco cresc.
Ldy.B.
masculine smell!
She comes back into the room to greet her visitors.
Tutti
f broadly
(largamente)
mf
f broadly
(largamente)
tr
sf
sf dim.

MISS WORDSWORTH
Good morn - ing!
LADY BILLOWS
shaking hands
Good morn - ing!
Good morn - ing!
MAYOR
Good
VICAR
Good morn - ing!
Str.
pp marked
sim.
pp heavy (pesante)
sim.
Miss W.
My La - - dy, good morn - ing!
Ldy.B.
Good morn - ing! Good morn - ing!
May.
morn - ing! My La - - dy, good morn - ing!
Vic.
My La - - dy, good morn - ing!
SUPER
Good morn - ing! My La - - dy, good morn - ing!
cresc.
sempre più f

 B. & H. 16241

14
Miss W
mf rhythmic (ritmico)
sf
This is the tenth of A-pril, The day your Ladyship planned For our second and fi-nal meeting....
FLORENCE
mf rhythmic (ritmico)
This is the tenth of A-pril, The day your Ladyship planned For our second and fi-nal meeting....
May.
mf rhythmic (ritmico)
This is the tenth of A-pril, The day your Ladyship planned For our second and fi-nal meeting....
Vic.
mf rhythmic (ritmico)
This is the tenth of A-pril, The day your Ladyship planned For our second and fi-nal meeting....
Sup.
mf rhythmic (ritmico)
This is the tenth of A-pril, The day your Ladyship planned For our second and fi-nal meeting....
14
W.
sf fp
fp
Str.
mf heavy (pesante)
Miss W.
sf
cresc.
.....We're here to see how we stand; For the Queen of the May must be appointed by us to-
Flo.
.....We're here to see how we stand; For the Queen of the May must be appointed by us to-
May.
.....We're here to see how we stand; For the Queen of the May must be appointed by us to-
Vic.
.....We're here to see how we stand; For the Queen of the May must be appointed by us to-
Sup.
.....We're here to see how we stand; For the Queen of the May must be appointed by us to-
fp
cresc.

Miss W.
day!
LADY BILLOWS
All ve-ry punctual. Glad to see it! Ear - ly worms!
Flo.
day!
May.
day!
Vic.
day!
Sup.
day!
broadly (largamente)
We've made our
Harp Timp.
15
Flo.
We've made our own in-ves-ti-ga - tions...... and bring you our no-mi-nees..........
Sup.
own in-ves-ti-ga - tions... and bring you our no-mi-nees.......... and we're
f broadly (largamente)

MISS WORDSWORTH
broadly
f (largamente)
We've made our
Flo.
And we're rea - dy, we're rea - dy, when -
VICAR
broadly
f (largamente)
We've made our own in - ves - ti - ga - tions
Sup.
sf tr
rea - dy, we're rea - dy when - e - - ver you
Miss W.
own in - ves - ti - ga - tions and bring you
Flo.
sf tr
- e - - - ver you please. We're
Vic.
and bring you our no - mi - nees
Sup.
please. We're rea - dy,

Miss W.
our..... no - mi - nees................................ and we're
Flo.
rea - dy, we're rea - dy, we're rea - dy when -
Vic.
.... and we're rea - dy, we're rea - dy, we're
Sup.
we're rea - dy, we're rea - dy, we're rea - dy,
Miss W.
rea - dy, we're rea - dy, when - e - - - ver you
Flo.
- e - - - ver you please.
MAYOR
broadly (largamente)
We've made our
Vic.
rea - dy, we're rea - dy, when - e - - - ver you
Sup.
we're rea - dy, we're rea - dy, rea - dy, rea - dy, rea - dy when you

Miss W.
please.
Flo.
ff
We've made our own in - ves - ti - ga - tions
May.
own in - ves - ti - ga - tions and bring you
Vic.
please, We're rea - dy, we're rea - dy,
Sup.
please. We've made our
ff
ff
ff
Miss W.
We've made our own in - ves - ti - ga - tions
Flo.
and bring you our no - mi - nees,
May.
our no - mi - nees, and
Vic.
we're rea - dy. We've made our
ff
Sup.
own in - ves - ti - ga - tions and bring you

They bring out their lists, while Lady Billows moves to sit at the table.*

* This instruction does not appear in the full score.

Miss W.
rea - dy, we're rea - dy when - e - - - - ver you
Flo.
rea - dy, we're rea - dy when - e - - - - ver you
May.
rea - dy, we're rea - dy when - e - - - - ver you
Vic.
rea - dy, we're rea - dy when - e - - - - ver you
Sup.
own in - ves - ti - ga - tions and we're rea - dy when - e - ver you
They seat themselves at the table around Lady Billows.
16
Lively
(Vivace) (𝅗𝅥 quicker than ♩ of preceding)
Miss W.
please.
LADY BILLOWS
Now then! Note book, Florence!
Flo.
please.
May.
please.
Vic.
please.
Sup.
please.
poco rit.
16
Lively
(Vivace) (𝅗𝅥 quicker than ♩ of preceding)

Ldy. B.
All know why we're here!
Fl.
Hn. Bsn.
(pp)
On-ly one i-tem on to-day's a-gen-da...
p
f
To choose a Queen of the May!
cresc.
17
(♩. = ♩ of preceding)
W. Str.
ff
with animation
f (con anima)
May Queen! May Queen!
W.
fp
Str.
ff
marked
(marcato)
There's a lot of sim-ple wis-dom in these old tra-
mf

Ldy. B.
-di-tions... like Hal-low-e'en, Har-vest Home, Chasing the Old Year
fp
pp
out of the Town........ and so on. Com-pe-ti-tion to
meno f
f
mf pp
be May Queen, when I was a girl, was a-ma-zing-ly
mf
mf pp
18
keen; A-mong the vil-lage girls, I mean. All dressed in
light (leggiero)
gay (giocoso)
Fl.
mf
p
cresc.
f pp

Ldy. B.
white, Met on the Green at noon on May the First, to par-
cresc.
-ade be-fore the Squire........................
dim.
Squire picked the win-ner, And sat be-side her dur-ing din-ner.......
più f
O .... you're.......... too young to re-mem-ber

freely
ff (ad lib.)
Ldy. B.
How these things were done.
fff
dim.
19 Quick (♪ = ♪)
(Allegro)
expansively
(liberamente)
p
I'm put-ting up a prize this year,—
Harp
W.
pp
Hn.
Harp
cresc.
Twen-ty-five sovereigns. Twenty-five! Con-si-der it my du-ty.
f
p
W.
mf
with force (con forza)
Must make vir-tue at-trac-tive, ex-cit-ing, de - sir -
W.
Str.
sf
cresc.
f

rall.
20
a little slower
(poco più lento)
with horror
(con orrore)
Ldy. B.
- a - ble for young..... peo-ple! Too ma-ny go-ings-on...
Harp
ppp
Str. (trem. pont.)
pp
p
Dir - ty things.....
ff
pp
ugh! Our birth-rate ris-es every week, Poor Doctor Jessop is
Hn.
mf
Bsn. D.B.
pp
heavy
(pesante)
slowly animating
(poco a poco animando)
p ma sempre cresc.
run off his feet... De - li - ver - ing new ba - bies to
poco a poco cresc.

Ldy. B.
Mothers of whom ex - ces-sive - ly few have ta - ken the trouble of vi-sit-ing you,
f
Vi-car!
with force (con forza)
Shocking business! No! I won't
w.w.
f very expressive
f heavy (pesante)
sf
have it!
più f
Town's in a state of complete mo - ral
più f
più f
più f
21 lively (animato)
f rapidly (rapido)
cha-os!
Well then... All in fa-vour sig-ni-fy...
ff
sf
cresc.
sf
fp

As they raise their hands, the clock chimes.
Ldy. B.
Usual manner...
quietly (tranquillo)
Hn. Fl. trem.
molto cresc.
ff pp
Glock.
f
p
U - na - ni-mous! Good! Let's have the suggestions...
6
6
ff
pp
ballad-like
Recit. (quasi ballata)
I'm wait-ing! First?
VICAR rising
freely
p (ad lib.)
The first sug-gestion on my
Piano
rhythmic
p (ritmico)
sim.
(always without pedal)
Vic.
list is a charm-ing lo - cal girl, who takes Com-mun-ion and ne - ver

* This instruction does not appear in the full score.

Miss W.
-mend E - li - za - beth New - ell, Whose Bo - ta - ny Notes are a
23
Quick (Allegro)
trea - sure.
FLORENCE
with force (con forza)
Was seen in the woods af - ter dusk...... with Tom Hood,...... last
Str. p
cresc.
LADY BILLOWS
Cross her name off! .... no good!
The Mayor stands.
Tues - day!
Ob.
Recit.
MAYOR f subito
rapidly (rapido)
There's Win - i - fred Brown, who works in the town As as - sist - ant to Missus Bell. I've
f Piano
sim.
(without ped.)
p sempre

dim.
May.
asked a - bout her, and peo-ple con-cur she be-haves on the average quite
dim.
24 Quick (Allegro)
FLORENCE p
cresc.
Ex - cept she went with her cou-sin from Kent For a trip in a dog-cart
May.
well.
Str. pp
cresc.
fp
Bsn.
Flo.
One Sun-day in Lent.
cresc.
f
Recit.
LADY BILLOWS f
clearing his throat
Speak up, Budd!
SUPER p
Er - humph! Er - humph!
I've lit-tle to
pp Piano
sim.

Sup.
say, My La-dy, so I'll make it short and sweet. The girl in my
25 Quick (Allegro)
FLORENCE
marked (marc.)
Ex -
Sup.
mind is a trea-sure you'll find, Her name is A - me-lia Keats.
25 Quick (Allegro)
Str. p
Flo.
cresc.
- pos - es her an - kles and legs bold as brass. Her skirt's far too
cresc.
Flo.
f sempre
short for a girl of her class! None of these
più f
ff
p sempre stacc.

LADY BILLOWS angrily
Won't ac-cept one of 'em! Cross 'em all out!
Flo.
four............ seems to me more than half up to
Ob. fz p
fz p
mf
Ldy B.
Can't waste time but-ter-ing par-snips... Want vir-gins_
Flo.
scratch As Queen of the May!
molto cresc.
sf
Ldy B.
not trol-lops!... More names?
ff
Hn.

a little more agitated
Recit.—(poco più agitato)
VICAR rising quickly
p
I have an - o - ther name or two I brought with
p Piano
sim.
Vic.
me in case the first was not ac - cep - ta - ble. What a - bout E - dith
26
Quick
(Allegro)
LADY BILLOWS
to Florence
f
Well, what a - bout her?
FLORENCE
f
Much too fligh - ty!
Vic.
cresc.
Chase?
She at -
Str. f
sf pp

with force
(con forza)
Flo.
When the post-man called one day she opened the
Vic.
- tends my Bi - ble group.....
f
more agitated
Recit. (più agitato)
MISS WORDSWORTH
Miss W.
Has
Flo.
door........ in her nigh - tie!
Fl.
ff
sf
Piano
p
Miss W.
a - ny - one thought of the shoe-maker's twins?... Joyce Ma - ry and her sis - ter? Most
sim.

27
Quick
(Allegro)
Miss W.
prac-ti-cal girls at han-di-crafts...
Flo.
grimly cresc.
I've heard of things from Mis-ter
Str. trem.
p
LADY BILLOWS
Both .... of them?
Budd a-bout them both.
SUPER
Take my Bi-ble oath!......
poco a poco cresc.
Vlc.
mf
Flo.
f
He can't re-peat what he caught them at... You'll par-don him,
Sup.
ffz
Ob.
sff p
f

always more agitated
Recit.–(sempre più agitato)
Flo.
milady...
Was
VICAR
There's that girl who works at Pi-per's Farm?
mf
sim.
Piano
Quick (Allegro)
MISS WORDSWORTH
28
express.
p
O sure - -
Flo.
lost one night, and then found in a barn!..........
MAYOR
f
The girl from the dai - ry?..
Quick (Allegro)
28
Str. pp
Miss W.
- ly there must .... be one to
Flo.
f
She won't re - fuse, Though not i-deal by a long, long chalk!
May.
.....
cresc.
D.B.
mf
cresc.

Recit.
Miss W.
choose!...
ff LADY BILLOWS
Then don't sug - gest her!
SUPER.
f
Peo-ple talk of Nan-cy
Cl.
ff
f
Piano
29
Quick
(Allegro)
FLORENCE
... the ba - kers daugh-ter?
No! ....
Sup.
Wa - ters, ... but I'm not sure...
Str. f
30
with force
(con forza)
Flo.
...... no! no! no! no! no! no! no!
Could - n't have her for Queen of the
VICAR
pp
sust.
My mind .... has
ppp
poco a poco cresc.

MISS WORDSWORTH pp
What can we
Flo.
May!
MAYOR f
She runs after Sid ..... who's my as-
Vic.
scoured the par-ish through, ... our lists are fin-ished.
Miss W.
do? sust. Not e-ven one girl ..... whom we can
May.
-sis-tant, and him af-ter her, ... both ve-ry per - sis-tent.
Miss W.
trust, ... cresc. not e-ven one in
May.
p sust. It is! .....
VICAR p cresc.
And must we cast our hope-ful glan - ces .....
SUPER pp sust.
I reck-on that's true! ..... cresc. I rec-kon that's

Miss W.
all the town?
Sad?
May.
Un - hap - py?
Vic.
down? Un - hap - py?
De - feat - ed?
Sup.
true!
Sad?
cresc. and sust.
De - feat - ed?
Be - fore our pro - ject is com -
cresc. and sust.
Sad?
Be - fore our pro - ject is com -
cresc. and sust.
Be - fore our pro - ject is com -
De - feat - ed?
f
Sad
molto cresc.

31
Miss W.
- plet - - ed!
FLORENCE
You've none.......... of you suc - ceed - ed!
May.
- plet - - ed!
Vic.
- plet - - ed!
Sup.
31
w.
dim.
All sit silent and glum.
dim.
sempre più p
ppp
32 Recit. — lamenting (lamentoso)
Miss W.
I teach.... my pu-pils they must strive
May.
How sad to see
Vic.
Oh bit-ter, bit-ter is the fruit Sprung from the seed of
32
Piano
sim.
with ped.

Miss W.
For mo-ral grace and truth. But they care lit-tle
May.
a de-cent town Lose its good name and sink
Vic.
sin: It feeds on poi-son at the root and
SUPER pp
Po - lice-men have a tick-lish task in stamping out a -
Miss W.
for ad - vice In head - strong days of youth.
May.
slow-ly, slow-ly, slow-ly down And ho-ver on the
Vic.
can-kers all with - in.
Sup.
- bu - ses............... For hu-man flesh is on - ly grass, and

Lady Billows begins to simmer and suddenly rises in rage.
33
Quick and agitated
(Allegro agitato) 𝅗𝅥 = 82
May
brink!
Sup.
dark-ness has its us-es!
Str. pp
marked
Harp
pp
p
mf
più f
cresc.
mf
f
G.P.
pp molto cresc.
LADY BILLOWS
furious
(furioso)
f
Is this all .... you can bring?
ff sempre
(sempre f)
ff
mf

Ldy. B.
Each sin - gle name
Reek - ing im - pur -
- i-ties, Ex - ud - ing mo - - - ral blame?
sf
mf
f
pp
molto cresc.
Is there no more than this to of-fer? Not
molto cresc.
p
one thing, not one thing, But
(sempre cresc.)
ff

34
Ldy. B.
stinks of sens - - ual
shame?
FLORENCE f echoing her mistress.
... But stinks of sens - ual
mf
shame!
Flo.
molto cresc.
ff
Are Lox-ford girls all......
whores?
None clean, none sure?
sf
mf

Ldy. B.
Las - civ - ious nan - ny goats,
Each one, each
sf
f
one im - pure?
p cresc.
I'll curb their
sf
f
pp
cresc.
pp
pas - sions, show them with a whip, with a
cresc.
whip, that laws of mo - rals
f

Ldy. B.
must en - dure.
FLORENCE f
That mo - rals must en -
mf
more quietly
p (più tranquillo)
Is
Flo.
dure!
dim.
(Harp gliss.)
p
pp
35
this the........ town where
Str.
pp marc. sempre
pp
3
3
3

Ldy. B.
I have lived and toiled, where I have lived and toiled?
pp
freely (ad lib.)
A Sodom and Gomorrah.
with the voice (colla parte)
a tempo
pp
Str. (sul pont.)
ppp
sf
pppp rall.
Ripe to be despoiled.
rall.
very animated (molto animato) (spoken)
cresc.
O spawning ground of horror!
pp cresc. sempre
Gong
8va

Ldy. B.
O spawn - ing ground of
pp cresc. sempre
hor - ror!
f
Shame to
p cresc. sempre
Lox - ford!
più f
Shame to
Lox - ford! Sty the fe - male
ff
f

Ldy. B.
sex has soiled!
FLORENCE ff
Sty the
ff
f
Flo.
fe - male sex has soiled... Sty the fe - male sex has
meno f
p
LADY BILLOWS f
Sty the . . .
The clock strikes four quarters and then
Flo.
soiled...
gliss.
Fl. Hn.
pp
pp
Glock.
the hour of eleven.
G. P.
2

36
LADY BILLOWS
pp senza voce
Fe - - - - male sex
FLORENCE
pp senza voce
Fe - - - - male sex
36
pp
Ldy. B.
has soiled . . .
Flo.
has soiled . . .
Lady Billows sits, exhausted by her own vehemence, among the unhappy committee.
più f
più f e molto cresc.
The Superintendent has a sudden brainwave.
ff
gliss.
gliss.
lunga
ppp

Recit.
SUPERINTENDENT
hesistant (esitando)
Beg-gin' your par-don, I'd like to say, Has a-ny-one heard of a
Piano
MISS WORDSWORTH
I........................ ne-ver
LADY BILLOWS
Fan-tas-tic!
FLORENCE
King....... of the May?
Sup.
King of the May?
Miss W.
did...
MAYOR
I sup-pose you'd crown Sid! ....
VICAR
Not in East Suf-folk...

May.
Sup.
p
May-be it seems a rum sort of no - tion
But it might help us out of the
p
LADY BILLOWS f
'Rum' it may be... 'help-ful,' no!
mf
Mere red herring, Budd!
Sup.
f
present commotion.
f
Just so!
f
p
Sup.
Her-ring's the name, and Her-ring's the lad —
Fel-low we're want-ing 's there to be had...
f

All are amazed at this suggestion.

37
Very quick ♩= 136
(Allegro molto)
with confidence
(con anima)
Sup.
Al - bert Her - ring's
(marked)
smooth
(legato)
p but heavy (ma pesante)
Str. ff
f
Bsn.
clean as new - mown hay: Ho - nest, truth - ful,
keen as Col - man's Mus - tard, as they say!
Str. ff
Ne - ver kicks up rough, as
p
(Bsn. f)

Sup.
most boys do. Al - bert's real good stuff: as
f
dim.
Sup.
good as gold, right through and through!
cresc.
ff
sf
dim.
rall.
Recit.
VICAR p
hesitant (esitando)
I know the boy you mean ...... but is he quite..?
smooth (legato)
pp
MAYOR p
I've seen him since he was a kid: He's al-ways lived next door to me...
Piano
pp

MISS WORDSWORTH
p
When he at-tend-ed school poor Al-bert was not bright at les - sons,... tho' quite ex -
Miss W.
- cep - tion - al for con - duct.
VICAR p
An in - of - fen - sive lad,—
MAYOR p
A splen - did son to Mis - sus Her - ring...
Vic.
sim - ple, of course...
LADY BILLOWS scornfully
f energetic (energico)
What pre-cise - ly has a grocer's lad to do with this dis-cus - sion?
ffz

brooding
slow
(lento)
p cresc.
Ldy.B.
Ri - di - cu - lous pro - po - sal! I'm cer - tain there are girls —
pp cresc.
poco accelerando - - - - - (accel.) - - - - - -
f
Ldy.B.
far - mer's daughters,.... may - be.... suit - a - ble for us. — Flo - rence...?
ff
FLORENCE
p
Hope - less, Mila - dy I've been round all the farms and
p
slowly
Flo.
small-hold-ings. Shock-ing re - sults!............
ppp
without ped.

significantly
pp (significativo)
Flo.
Coun - try vir-gins, if there be such, think too lit-tle and see too
38
Slow and sad (tempo rubato)
(Lento mesto e rubato)
LADY BILLOWS p
I'm a ve-ry dis - ap-point - ed
much.
Vlc.
pp very expressive
cresc.
p
Str. ppp express.
Ldy. B.
pp
wo-man!
slightly animating
(poco animando)
cresc.
più cresc.
Ei - ther we a - ban - don the Fest - i - val..... or...
SUPERINTENDENT
Al - bert Her - ring!
f
gliss.

* This instruction does not appear in the full score.

Vic.
poco cresc.
.... ru - bies........ amethyst, Rich-er than... wealth,....
poco cresc.
Vic.
.... wis - dom.... righteousness!
singing
(cantabile)
Vic.
Is Al - bert vir - tu-ous? Yes? or no?
w.
ppp
Harp poco marcato
Vic.
That is all we need .... to know.

40
MISS WORDSWORTH
pp
Al - bert is vir - - - - tu - ous,
FLORENCE
pp
They say he's vir - - - - tu - ous,
MAYOR
pp
He's ve - ry vir - - - - tu - ous,
VICAR
slightly marked
Is Al-bert vir-tu-ous? Al-bert vir-tu-ous?
SUPER
pp
What, Al - bert vir - - - - tu - ous?
40
sust.
mp express.
sempre arpeggiando
Miss W.
yes, I know, He is tru - ly,
Flo.
as boys go, Ev' - ry bo - dy
May.
don't you know, Ev' - ry bo - dy
Vic.
Yes or no? Yes......... or no? That............... is all we need to know, that is
Sup.
That I know. Cer - tain - ly he

Miss W.
tru - - ly so.
Flo.
tells .... me so.
May.
thinks .... him so.
Vic.
all .... we need .... to know, That is all we need to
pp
Sup.
must .... be so.
dim.
rit.
Miss W.
ppp
'Her-ring'.
LADY BILLOWS pp
'Al-bert...' what's his name?
pppp
'Her-ring'...
Flo.
ppp
'Her-ring'.
May.
ppp
'Her-ring'.
Vic.
know...
ppp
'Her-ring'.
Sup.
ppp
'Her-ring'.
rit.
ppp

* This instruction does not appear in the full score.

Ldy.B.
On the First of May, on the First of May.
FLORENCE
light
(leggiero)
Let's go and tell him, An-nouncing our de-ci-sion, Warn
Ob.
Ldy.B.
On the First of
Flo.
him to be rea-dy on the First of May
cresc.
sim.
Ldy.B.
May, on the First, the First of May!
Flo.
on the First of May, the First of May!
dim.

43
Ldy.B.
Flo.
VICAR
Vic.
Bsn.
Harp
p
f
sim.
light
(leggiero)
.... On the First of May,........................
.... On the First of May! .... An-nounc-ing our de -
Most sat - is - fac - to - ry, Mag - ni - fi-cent so - lu - tion, For....
.... on .... the First of May!................................
- ci - sion, Warn.... him to be rea - dy, An-nounc - ing our de -
...... the co - ro - na - tion, Mag - ni - fi - cent so - lu - tion for the

MISS WORDSWORTH f
So en - -
Ldy.B.
pp
.... Re - mark - a - ble po - si - tion, cause..
Flo.
pp
- ci - sion for the First of May!
Vic.
pp
co - ro - na - tion on the First of May.
Fl.
Harp
pp
light
(leggiero)
Miss W.
- cou - rag - ing for all our dear young peo - ple "Vir -
Ldy.B.
...... a great sen - sa - tion on the First of
Flo.
pp
Let's go and
Vic.

Miss W.
Ldy.B.
Flo.
Vic.
- tue is re - ward - ed On the First of
May. May King!
tell him, an - nounc - ing our de - ci - sion for the
On the First of
p
pp
May." For all our dear young people, "Vir - tue is re-ward-ed, is re -
May King! May King! May King!
First of May. On
f MAYOR
Ur - ban Dis - trict Coun - cil - lors, All o - ver Eastern Suf - folk, En -
May, on the First of May,
cresc.
mf
sim.

44
Miss W.
dim.
-ward-ed on the First of May!"
Ldy.B.
f dim.
On the
Flo.
ff dim.
the First of May!
May.
ff dim.
-vy lit-tle Lox-ford On the First of May, the First of
Vic.
ff dim.
On the First of May!
44
ff dim.
sim.
sim.
Miss W.
p
Ah!
Ldy.B.
pp
First, the First of May re-mark-a-ble po-si-tion, cause a
Flo.
pp
An-nounc-ing our de-ci-sion, warn him
May.
(dim.) pp
May! All o-ver Eas-tern Suf-folk, en-vy
Vic.
pp clearly (distinto)
Mag-ni-fi-cent so-lu-tion for the
stacc.
Harp
Str.
pp

cresc.
Miss W.
(Ah)
Ldy.B.
great sen - sa - tion on the First of, on the First of, on the First of,
Flo.
to be rea - dy on the First of, on the First of, on the First of,
May.
lit - tle Lox - ford on the First of, on the First of, on the First of,
Vic.
co - ro - na - tion on the First of, on the First of, on the First of,
SUPERINTENDENT f
Er - humph! Er - humph! Er - humph! Er-humph! Er -

45
Miss W.
(ah)
Ldy.B.
sfp
First of, First of
May!
Flo.
sfp
First of, First of
May!
May.
sfp
First of, First of
May!
Vic.
sfp
First of, First of
May!
Sup.
ff
- humph!
All the po - lice force, all the po -
45
mf
cresc.
Bsn.
Harp

Miss W.
mf cresc.
On .... the First of
Ldy.B.
Flo.
p cresc.
On .... the First of May, on..........
May.
mf cresc.
On............... the First of
Vic.
p cresc.
On .... the First of May, on..........
Sup.
sempre ff; heavy (pesante)
- lice force, Will have to be on du - ty, Keep - ing things in or - der, Will
Fl.
Ob.
mf cresc.

Miss W.
May, on .... the First of May! ....
Flo.
.... the First of May, of May! ....
May.
May, on .... the First of May! ....
Vic.
.... the First of May, of May! ....
Sup.
have to be on du-ty, Keep - ing things in or-der, On the First of
f cresc.
cresc.
Miss W.
.... of
Flo.
.... of
May.
.... of
Vic.
.... of
Sup.
May, the First of May! ....
ff

46
Slow
(Largo) (♩ = 𝅗𝅥 of proceding)
Miss W.
ff
May!
LADY BILLOWS
Ldy.B.
f brilliant
very marked
Re-joice, my friends, and be .... ex-ceed-ing glad! ....
Flo.
ff
May!
May.
ff
May!
Vic.
ff
May!
Sup.
ff
May!
46
Slow
(Largo) (♩ = 𝅗𝅥 of proceding)
Cl.
Hn.
ffz
f
fp
Timp.
sempre f

Miss W.
Ldy. B.
Flo.
May.
Vic.
Sup.
ff
sf
Vir - tue has sig - nall'd forth Her cham-pion and de-fen - - -
ffz
W.W.
Str.
Harp

Miss W.
- der!
Hum - ble in looks, of low-ly
Ldy.B
A vil-lage lad, a vil - - - lage lad!
Flo.
- der!
Hum - ble in looks, of low-ly
May.
- der!
Hum - ble in looks, of low-ly
Vic.
- der!
Hum - ble in looks, of low-ly
Sup.
- der!
Hum - ble in looks, of low-ly
ff
f
fp

Miss W.
birth, beneath whose a - pron beats a heart, re - pel Temp-ta - tion,......
Ldy.B.
.... To conquer Sin, To
Flo
birth, beneath whose a - pron beats a heart, re - pel Temp-ta - tion,.....
May.
birth, beneath whose a - pron beats a heart, re - pel Temp-ta - tion,......
Vic.
birth, beneath whose a - pron beats a heart, re - pel Temp-ta - tion,......
Sup.
birth, beneath whose a - pron beats a heart, re - pel Temp-ta - tion,......
sf
ff
f

Miss W.
f
f
p sust.
.... re-pel Temp-ta - tion, Ren - der back to Vir - tue,
Ldy.B.
meno f
conquer Sin, To conquer Sin, ren - der back to Vir - tue,
Flo.
f
f
p sust.
.... re-pel Temp-ta - tion, Ren - der back to Vir - tue,
May.
f
f
p sust.
.... re-pel Temp-ta - tion, Ren - der back to Vir - tue,
Vlc.
f
f
p sust.
.... re-pel Temp-ta - tion, Ren - der back to Vir - tue,
Sup.
f
f
p sust.
.... re-pel Temp-ta - tion, Ren - der back to Vir - tue,
ff sec.

Miss W.
p
render back to Virtue what she entrusts to him,..... what she en-
Ldy. B.
(p)
.... ren-der back to Vir-tue........
Flo.
p
ren-der back to Vir-tue what she en-trusts to him,..... what she en-
May.
p
ren-der back to Vir-tue what she en-trusts to him,..... what she en-
Vic.
p
ren-der back to Vir-tue what she en-trusts to him,..... what she en-
Sup.
p
ren-der back to Vir-tue what she en-trusts to him,..... what she en-

47
Miss W.
ff
- trusts to him!......
Her crown of sim-ple and re -
Ldy.B.
f
With-out res-pect of gen - - der,
Flo.
ff
- trusts to him!......
Her crown of sim-ple and re -
May.
ff
- trusts to him!......
Her crown of sim-ple and re -
Vic.
ff
- trusts to him!.....
Her crown of sim-ple and re -
Sup.
ff
- trusts to him!.....
Her crown of sim-ple and re -
47
cresc.
mf
ff

Miss W.
ff
- ful - gent splendour! Her crown of sim - ple splendour!
Ldy.B.
f
ff
.... With-out res-pect of gen - der,............................ With-out res -
Flo.
ff
- ful - gent splendour! Her crown of sim - ple splendour!
May.
ff
- ful - gent splendour! Her crown of sim - ple splendour!
Vic.
ff
- ful - gent splendour! Her crown of sim - ple splendour!
Sup.
ff
- ful - gent splendour! Her crown of sim - ple splendour!
f
ff

Miss W.
fff
of gen - - - - -
Ldy.B.
ff
-pect of gen - - - - - - - - ....
with-out respect of gen -
Flo.
fff
of gen - - - - -
May.
fff
of gen - - - - -
Vic.
fff
of gen - - - -
Sup.
fff
of gen - - - -
sfp molto cresc.
fffz

Interlude

48
Very moderate but rhythmic ♩= 96-104
(Molto moderato ma ritmico)
CURTAIN
Miss W.
- der!
Ldy. B.
- der!
Flo.
- der!
May.
- der!
Vic.
- der!
Sup.
- der!
48
Very moderate but rhythmic ♩= 96-104
(Molto moderato ma ritmico)
pp
W.
pp
Perc.
cresc.
fz

ff
f marked
Str. ff
dim.
pp
49
pp
pp

Str.
poco p ma marc.
tr
(tr)
50
W.
Str.
p poco a poco
cresc.
stringendo
(tr)
f cresc.
f
a tempo
8va
Picc.
ff
dim.

51
Vl.
6
6
poco dim.
mf
Vc.
p
pp
pp
52
ppp
cresc.
f express.
dim.

53
lively
(animato)
Str. harm.
sempre
dim.
smooth
(legato)
singing
(cantabile)
pp
p
sim.
poco cresc.
f
p
pp
cresc.
ff
p
pp

54
8
w.
ff
move on!
(avanti!)
ff sempre
55
ff
Str.
3
f
Perc.
p
pp
Fl.
Bsn.
56
Clt. (innocently)
mf
57
Fl.
Str.
trem. pp

molto cresc.
f
ff
mf molto cresc.
Perc.
ff
mf
58
lively
(animato)
ff
Str.
W.W.
Hn.
ff express.

sf trem.
ff
ff
8

cresc.
8
cresc.
59
CURTAIN
8
fff
ff
dim.
mf

Scene II. Mrs Herring's greengrocery shop.

Emmie, Cis and Harry are outside the shop, singing as they play ball against the lower half of the door. The upper half of the door is open.

Em.
Cis
Har.
Bounce me quick, Bounce me to A-rith-me-tick! (claps) Bounce me high,
Ball
p
pp
mf
Em.
Cis
Har.
Bounce me low, Bounce me up to Je-ri-cho! Bounce me slow, Bounce me quick,
Ball
Em.
Cis
Har.
Bounce me to A-rith-me-tick! (claps) Bounce me high, Bounce me low,
Ball
p
pp
mf

The ball comes flying through the door and rolls across the shop. The children peep through the door.

⊕ always whole-tone-trills.

Harry looks round the shop.
Em.
f
All right?
G.P.
Cis
f
All right?
G.P.
Har.
f
Ow!
G.P.
tr
Clt.
ffz
G.P.
pp
62
Harry finds the ball.
Em.
f (whispered)
There it is,
by that old box!
pp
pp cresc.
Str. pizz.
HARRY
f
Catch!
He throws it to the girls.
Ob.
f
espress.
dim.
Harry sees a box of apples, and creeps towards it.
a little hesitant
(un poco esitando)
Hn. (con sord.)
pp
G.P.
ppp
Str.

animating slightly
(poco animando)
Picc.
8va
molto cresc.
fpp
63
a tempo
Harry passes some apples out to the girls.
EMMIE
poco f
Look
CIS.
poco f
Give us some too, Har-ry! Taa!
63
8
Harp
marcatiss.
Em.
out! S'pose Al-bert came, s'pose Al-bert came?
HARRY
f
Sil-ly old
8
cresc.
pp
Har.
fool! Can't catch me!
8
molto cresc.
sim.

EMMIE
Ooh! .... what love - ly ap-ples!
CIS
Love - ly
f dim.
pp
Em.
Cis
ap-ples!
Some more? ....
HARRY
Some more? ....
Some more? ....
cresc. molto
Sid arrives, scattering the girls as he comes through the door. He sees Harry and tries to catch him.
SID.
Come out .... of that, my lad!
Shop Bell
sf
ff

Sid catches Harry, holds him tight and starts emptying his pockets.

Em.
Cis
HARRY
(screaming)
Ow!
Leg-go!....
Sid
Lit-tle beggar!
Damn good
hi - ding's what you need!
No-sey Parker too!
No-sey Par - ker!
Empty your

Em.
Cis
HARRY
Sid
Leave him be!
Leave him be!
Leave him be! ....
Leave him be!
Leg - go of
me!
pockets!
Is that the lot?
Well then, get
cresc.
ff
sf
65
ffz Sid throws Harry out of the door.
The children run away.
poco a poco dim. -
Ah!
We'll 'tell his dad _
Ah!
We'll tell his dad _
Har.
fff
Ow ....
OUT!
f express. e dim.

dim.
Em.
Sid from the butcher's knock'd Har - ry a - bout! Sid from the butcher's knock'd
dim.
Cis
Sid from the butcher's knock'd Har - ry a - bout! Sid from the butcher's knock'd
6
f dim.
p
Em.
Har - ry a - bout! Sid from the butcher's knock'd Har-ry a - bout!.... Sid!
Cis
Har - ry a - bout! Sid! Sid from the
p dim.
pp
Perc.
Sid shouts towards the inner door of the shop.
lunga
66 at the same speed (l'istesso tempo)
pp
Em.
Sid! ....
pp
lunga
Cis
butcher's! .... Sid! ....
66 at the same speed (l'istesso tempo)
lunga
dim.
ppp
Str.
f

Sid helps himself to an apple.
SID
Shop! Hi! Al-bert!
ff express.
Sid
Shop! Hi!
Al-bert!
There is a thud against the door, and Albert comes slowly in backwards carrying a large sack.
67
Very much slower
(Molto più lento)
rall.
very smooth
(legatiss.)
W.
Str.
heavy
(pesante)

Recit.
SID
There........ you are! — Just caught young Har-ry, pinch-ing things.
pp
Sid helps Albert to lower the sack.
Sid
How d'you carry a weight like that a-lone? Cor!.......... must be twenty stone or more!
Piano
(rall.)
p (sim.)
same speed as before
(in tempo precedente)
ALBERT
It's a hun-dred-weight of tur-nips.
Sid
I see... Strong Man Act!
rapidly
(rapido)
Sid
Can I have three box-es of mixed herbs, please, chum?
pp
mf

Albert goes behind the counter to serve Sid.

a little slower
(poco più lento)
Alb.
Gambling's not in my line. Mum wouldn't like it!
Sid
f
Ne - ver you mind.
pp
Heads or tails? Come on, you call.
No, real - ly I won't, thanks all the same.
But why? Be -
- cause of Mum? Won't she let you have a - ny fun?
dim.
Fairly quick
(Allegretto)
ALBERT
poco f
Mum's tee -
pp sempre
Did you e - ver have a pint at the lo - cal?
Str.

Alb.
Sid
- to - tal...
Strict in her
Or go out with a whip-pet af-ter rab-bits?
piu f
ha - bits...
Do.................... stop this
Did you ne-ver try tak-ing a girl for a walk?
piu f
cresc.
talk!
I don't like it at
gaily
piu f (giocoso)
cresc.
Or dance to the band at the Ju-bi-lee Hall? Or
cresc.

Alb.
all! I just don't like it at all!
Sid
dance to the band? Or dance to the band at the
Alb.
not at all!............
Sid
Ju-bi-lee Hall? You will! you will! once you've broke the a-pron strings!
68
more lively ♩= 132
(piu vivo)
Sid
Tick-ling a trout, poach-ing a hare, Flight-ing wild geese is
cresc.
Clt. (brillant)
pp
Sid
pretty good sport for a chap to en - joy. Liv-ing without a re - gu-lar
Str.
pp
Clt.

Sid
share of pleasures like these is hard to support for your kind of a boy. But
courting a girl is the King of all sports in a class of its own .... Where there
aren't a-ny rules so long as she's caught and you catch .... her a - lone.
Girls mean .... Spring six .... days a week ....
Str. pp
Clt.
pp cresc.
cresc.
light
pp (leggiero)
ppp
pp cresc. molto
Timp.
69
with a swing
(con slancio)
sempre f
fz
Str.
ff express.

Sid
...... and twice on.......... Sun - days, The whole year round........., the win - ter
p cresc.
ffz
through. Girls mean:.... games of........... hide and seek.....
w.w.
ff
sf
pp
f
...... On sum-mer.... evenings, When some-one's bound.......... To fall for
p cresc.
ffz
you! Girls mean:.... prowl - ing.......... round in bleak...
poco a poco dim.
ff
sf
pp
f

Sid
...... and win - try .... wea - ther .... whis - p'ring, ... whis - p'ring, ... whis - p'ring,
Ped.
very sweetly
pp (dolcissimo)
"I love you, I love you, ... I love you, love .....
pp
(falsetto)
ppp
mf
ppp
ppp
Recit.
ALBERT
p
Sid, I'm sor - ry, but I've got a lot to do.
f
you!"
Oh! don't you worry ...... I'm
70
as before Nancy looks in through the top door.
(come sopra)
just off!
f
I'm bu - sy too.
Str.
f
w.w. f
più f

Sid opens the bottom door for Nancy to enter. She carries a shopping basket.

Sid
Al-bert who start-ed the sub-ject, of course... You want to watch Al - bert-
f
fz
NANCY
f
You ought to have some-thing bet-ter to do ....
Sid
pp
He's a ve-ry dark horse!
ppp
mf
Nan.
.... than gos - sip - ing here.
mf
Aren't you work - ing to - day?
p
SID.
f
I've been spinning a-round like a humming top Since I opened the shop at eight o' clock.
ff
dim.
tr

NANCY
with force
f (con forza)
Well, come and serve me, I'm in a hur-ry!
Sid
p
And you know what they say a-bout 'work and no play!'
pp
f
f
Nan.
with dignity
p (con dignita)
I've come for a piece of best Eng-lish beef.
Sid picks up a box of peaches.
Sid
There's no need to worry, there's no need to wor-ry!
f
mf
pp
Ped.
She takes one.
Nan.
Oo, may I real-ly?
ALBERT
Those are six-pence each!
Sid
p
Have a nice peach!
slow

Alb.
Two peaches at six - pence,.... that's a shil-ling, please.
Sid
Take two, I'll stand the damage.
I
(sec.)
Ped.
light (leggiero)
think I can just a - bout man - age to squeeze out a bob from the
NANCY
I won't eat them now. They're so ripe they might splash!
firm's pet-ty cash.
71
Fairly quick
(Allegretto)
Harp
Str.
express.
with feeling
(con sentimento)
You can bring them to night, and we'll each take a bite, To fla-vour our

mimicking him
(con parodia!)
Nan.
That sounds just.... de -
with charm
(grazioso)
Sid
kiss - es with a dash of peach bit - ters!
72
With movement ♩= 76
(Con moto)
- li - cious!
Meet me at quar-ter past eight in the street,..... don't be late or I'll
Hn.
Fl.
Cl.
ppp sweetly (dolce)
Yes! if you promise to wait in the street..
whis-tle under your window.
Vl.
8va
gliss.
sim.

Nan.
cresc.
..... if I'm late and not whis-tle under my win-dow.
For Mum will be
8va
p
ppp poco cresc.
cu - ri-ous, and Dad will be fu - ri-ous, to hear whist-ling un-der our
f
molto f
win-dow!
pp sust.
I'll
SID.
pp sust.
Do
dim.
pp

Nan.
Alb.
Sid
ALBERT to himself, uneasily
poco a poco cresc.
p but marked (ma marc.)
try to be there if I pos - si - bly
I do wish they would clear..... right a-way from our shop, For it's hard not to
try to be there if you pos - si - bly
can, For the night will be fine and
o - ver - hear. ....There'll be trou-ble I fear should my mo-ther ap-pear...... and dis-
can, For the night will be fine and
f
dim.
pp
clear...
- cov-er them flirt - - ing, flirting here!
clear...
73
Easily moving 𝅗𝅥 = 60
(Andante con moto)
Picc.
pp rhythmic (ritmico)
D.B. (pizz.)

Nan.
Sid
very smooth
pp (legatiss.)
sempre pp
We'll walk to the spin-ney up o - ver the
We'll walk to the spin-ney up o - ver the
(tr)
Com - mon, Arm in arm, my hand in your pock-et, Re -
Com - mon, Arm in arm, your hand in my pock-et, Re -
cresc.
- fresh - ing our selves in the plea - sures of love.
- fresh - ing our selves in the plea - sures of love.
pp
dim. l.h.
tr#
5

very smooth
pp (legatiss.)
Nan.
The moon will be shin-ing, The
pp very smooth (legatiss.)
Sid
The moon will be shin-ing, The
(tr)
sempre pp
sky will be star-ry, As we walk, my hand in your pocket, Re-
sempre pp
sky will be star-ry, As we walk, your hand in my pocket, Re-
cresc.
-fresh-ing our-selves in the plea-sures of love.
cresc.
-fresh-ing our-selves in the plea-sures of love.
pp
cresc.
dim. l.h.
tr
pp
Clt.
Bsn.
pp a little heavier
(poco più pesante)

74
Nan.
ALBERT (aside)
Sid
Alb.
pp always sust.
p express. and sust.
pp always sust.
And if it is rain-ing we'll share an um-brel-la, As we walk, my hand in your pock-et, re-fresh-ing our-selves in the plea-
And I shall be sleep-ing a-lone in my at-tic! As they walk, her hand in his pock-et, re-fresh-ing them-selves in the plea-
And if it is rain-ing we'll share an um-brel-la, As we walk, your hand in my pock-et, re-fresh-ing our-selves in the plea-
(tr)
cresc.
cresc. molto
f
ff

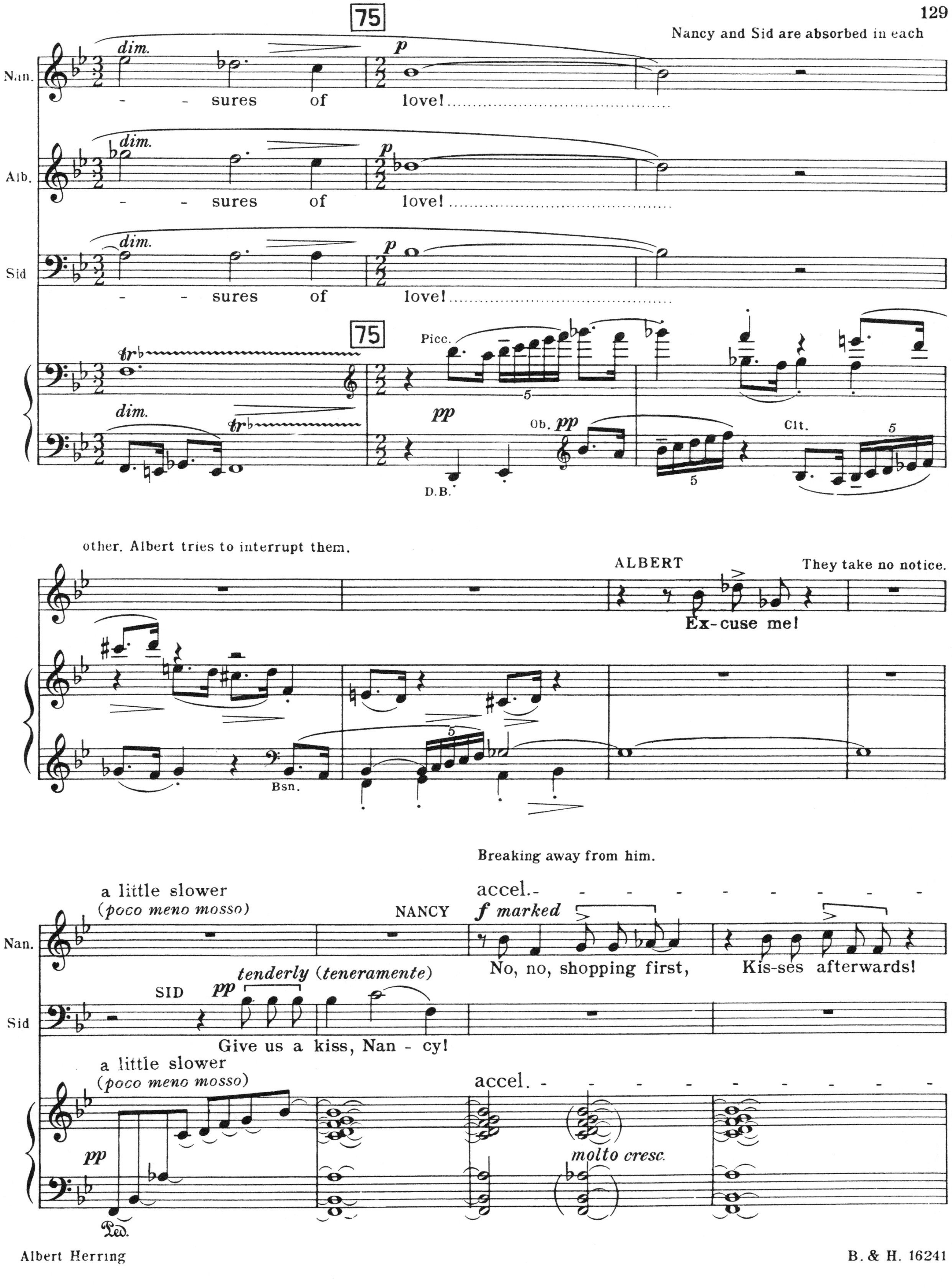
75
Nancy and Sid are absorbed in each
Nan.
dim.
p
- - sures of love!
Alb.
dim.
p
- - sures of love!
Sid
dim.
p
- - sures of love!
75
Picc.
dim.
pp
Ob. pp
Clt.
D.B.
other. Albert tries to interrupt them.
ALBERT
They take no notice.
Ex-cuse me!
Bsn.
Breaking away from him.
a little slower
(poco meno mosso)
NANCY
accel.
f marked
Nan.
No, no, shopping first, Kis-ses afterwards!
SID
pp
tenderly (teneramente)
Sid
Give us a kiss, Nan - cy!
a little slower
(poco meno mosso)
accel.
pp
molto cresc.
Ped.

Sid and Nancy go off gaily together. Albert dashes out of the shop after them.

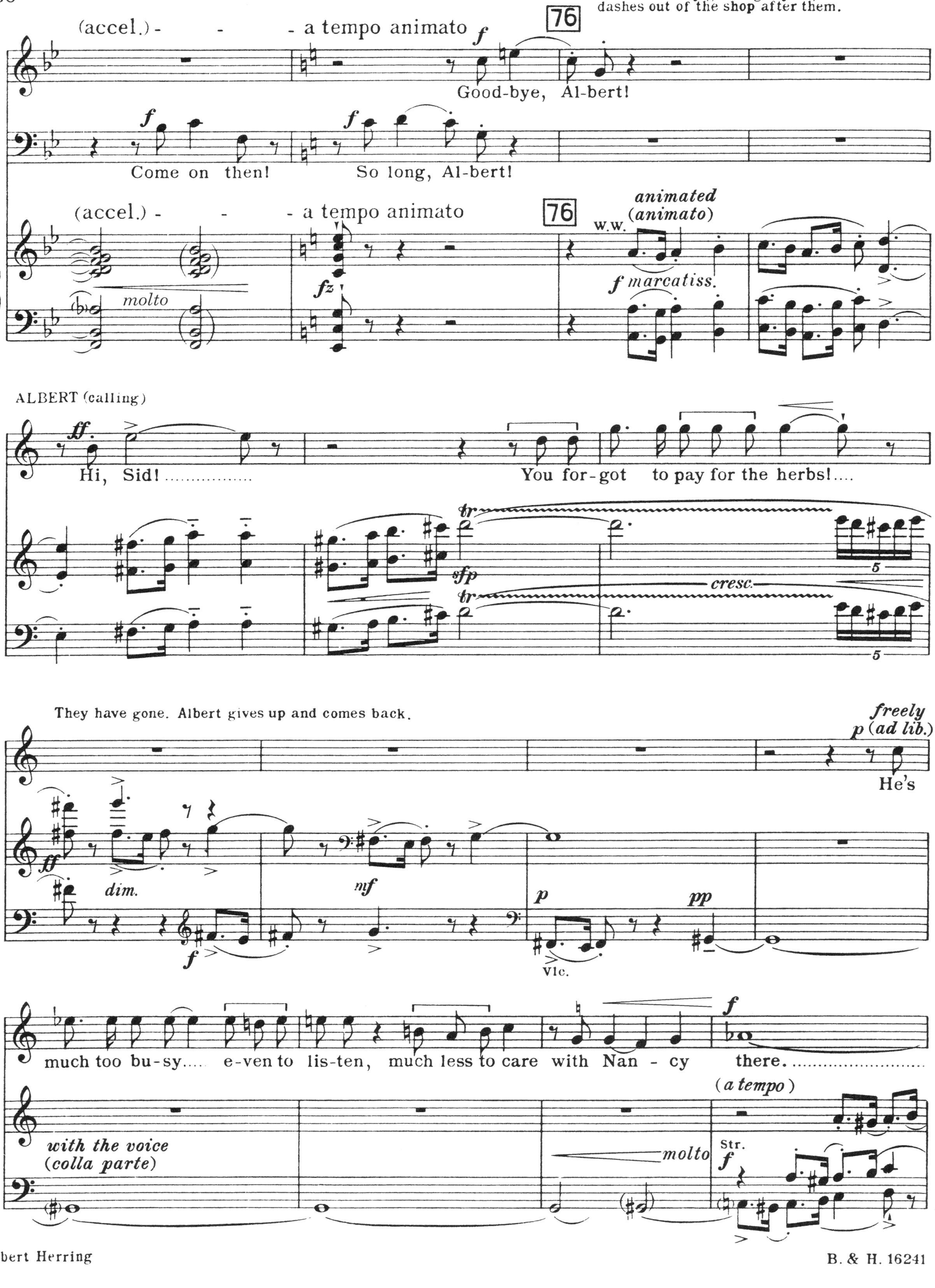

Alb.
freely
p (ad lib.)
I won-der, is he right,...when he says I miss all the fun,
mf
dim.
pp
p
Be-cause of Mum?
f
p cresc. molto
Determined
(Risoluto)
very marked
sf molto marc.
Yes! Mum's un-
ffz
and freely
e liberamente)
- common keen a-bout the need of liv-ing chaste and clean in word and deed. For what?
f (pizz.)
p
Timp. gliss.
più marcato
Each morn-ing... I.... get up... at... six and ti-dy up the
f

Alb.
stock, En-thu-si-as-ti-cal-ly fix price la-bels round the shop. For what?
mf
Timp.
energetic
(energico)
It's not ve-ry thrill-ing to live a-mong box-es and
f
bas - kets.... of ve - ge - ta - bles, flowers and sea - son - al
cresc.
fruits, I'm ex - pert at jobs...... like weigh - ing up
pun-nets of rasp-ber-ries.... And knowing when root-crops are like-ly to

dim.
Alb.
shoot_ For what? For what? For what? For what?
Slow and quiet 𝅗𝅥 = 48
(Lento e tranquillo)
simply (semplice)
molto rall.
It seems as clear as clear can be that Sid's i -
Str.
ppp sust., express.
- deas .... Are ve - ry much too crude for Mo - ther to ap -
più
- prove. And yet I'd real - ly like to try that kind of
W.W.

Alb.
life .... And see how it com-pares with serv-ing cus - to - mers.
Emmie rushes violently into the shop.
Recit. EMMIE
f fast (presto)
Shop bell
Mum wants two penn'orth of pot-herbs to make a stew in a
sf
77
Fast (Presto)
Em.
hur - ry, Mis - ter!
ALBERT
Where's your bas - ket?
Fl.
pp marked
Harp
Recit.
f rapidly (rapido)
Have - n't got one, bust it! My sis - ter went and lost it!
a tempo
pp

Recit.
Em.
Taa! That 'll be sa-fer than taking them
ALBERT p
I'll put 'em in pa - per.
a tempo
Recit.
Em.
loose. Got ex-tra 'o - li-days!
Alb
No school to-day? What e - ver
Fl.
pp
a tempo
78
Em.
On ac-count of Miss Weaver, our Bo-ta-ny Teach-er, went camping at Easter,
Alb.
for?
78
pp
cresc.
D.B.(pizz.)

confidentially
(intimo)
Em.
p
...... got scarlet fe-ver.
She was sharing our tent when she
f
dim.
ppp
came out all spotty, so they sent us all home with a let-ter ex-plain-ing they
wouldn't expect us at school for a week in case we're in - fec - tious!
cresc.
cresc.
p
Recit.
broadly
(largamente)
f
a tempo
It sounds a bit pot-ty, but we're not complain-ing.
ALBERT
p
Tuppence, please!
ff
pp

Emmie dashes off with her parcel.
Recit.
Em.
Don't mind farthings, do you? Thanks, Mister! Taa!
Alb.
..... Here you are.
79 As before
(Come sopra)
sweetly (dolce)
pp (Tutti)
cresc.
f
ALBERT
Oh, may - be soon I'll have the chance to get a -
ppp
cresc.
sf
Alb.
- way... And gol - ly! Gol - ly! It's a -
f
dim.
ffz
ff
f dim.
mf dim.

Alb.
-bout time, It's a - bout time, –
p
Gol - ly!
It's a - bout time, –
p express. e dim.
pp
pp
a - bout time...
80
Very moderate
(Molto moderato)
Florence comes past the window and into the shop.
(♩ = slower than ♩ of preceding.) ♩ = 104
Str. pp
heavy
Hn. (pesante)
p cresc.
Shop bell.
Recit.
FLORENCE f
Good morning, young man!
p
Good morn-ing, Miss Pike!
fp
with force
(con forza)
Flo.
I want if I can to talk to your Mum.
p
I'll call her at
p

Recit.
Flo.
The reason I've come is more urgent than those!
Alb.
once, but she's washing the clothes.
Albert calls through the inner door.
MUM (off)
What? Who is it?
Alb.
Mum! You're wanted.
Miss Florence Pike is here on a vis-it!
Coming back.
Alb.
Just dry-ing her hands.
Would you care to sit down?
FLORENCE
No, thank you. I'll stand.
I must-n't stay long.
81
Mum bustles in, drying her hands on her apron.
Ob.

MUM
affectedly
(affettato)
I'm sor-ry to keep you,— And how do you do?
Mum
Nice sun-ny day............ for the time of year too! ....
(♩. = ♩)
formally
FLORENCE
with force
(con forza)
Her La-dy-ship is
p
Flo.
on the way with Miss Wordsworth and the Vi - car, Messrs Budd and
82
(♩. = preceding ♩)
più f
MUM
What did you say? Vi - sit - ing
Flo.
Up-fold too, to vi-sit you here.
82
(♩ = preceding ♩)
più f

Mum
us? ....
But they can't come in here!
A shop's not the place for
Mum
peo - ple like them!
cresc.
And I
FLORENCE molto marc.
We shall get on much
p
mf
pp
Mum
can't have them in - to the par - lour to - day,
I'm air - ing the
Flo.
quicker ....
If you will be si - lent ....
cresc.

(ossia)
Mum
washing, air - ing it there!............
Flo.
...... and lis-ten to me! ....> The de-ci-sion they bring concerns
poco cresc.
83 (♩. = preceding ♩)
ff
Con-cerns Al - bert!...
Al-bert, as they will explain for them - selves.
ALBERT
f
Concerns me,............... do you
Oh! Don't say that Al-bert's in trou-ble some way?
Be
Alb.
say!?
(♩. = ♩)

Flo.
cresc.
quiet now! Are you rea-dy? Here they come! ....
mf cresc. molto
Lady Billows crosses the window, accompanied by Miss Wordsworth, the Mayor, Vicar and Superintendent Budd. They take
A little slower ♩= 96
(Un poco più lento)
Str.
sff f
sim.
up formal positions inside the shop to announce their news.
cresc.
LADY BILLOWS to Albert.
84
f martial (marziale)
We bring great news to
ff
Harp
Ldy. B.
you Up-on this hap-py day; Pa-tron-age and fame ap-plaud your

MISS WORDSWORTH
ff
De-clar-ing you Lox - ford King of the May!
Ldy. B.
sf
name!
FLORENCE
ff
De-clar-ing you Lox - ford King of the May!
MUM
pp
They're talking to you, Albert!
ALBERT
pp
I
MAYOR
ff
De-clar-ing you Lox - ford King of the May!
VICAR
ff
De-clar-ing you Lox - ford King of the May!
SUPER
ff
De-clar-ing you Lox - ford King of the May!
sim.
sf mf
fpp

Flo.
p
You've been cho - sen as May King,
Alb.
don't quite get their mean-ing...
Cho - sen as
Flo.
As May King!
Yes, you!
f
Hush!
MUM
f
Oh, Al-bert! Oh, Al - bert!
Alb.
what?
What! Me?
poco cresc.
f
85
LADY BILLOWS
f
We plan to ce - le - brate By crowning you up - on May Day af - ter - noon, that's fair - ly
ff

MISS WORDSWORTH
Not long to... wait! Just till A - pril's gone!
Ldy.B.
soon. ....
FLORENCE
Not long to... wait! Just till A - pril's gone!
MUM
Excuse me asking,
MAYOR
Not long to... wait! Just till A - pril's gone!
VICAR
Not long to... wait! Just till A - pril's gone!
SUPER
Not long to... wait! Just till A - pril's gone!
sim.
86
Mum
What's this crown-ing for?
ALBERT
I'd like to know that too!
VICAR
In ho - nour of your
86

MISS WORDSWORTH
p
Re - ward for chas - ti - ty!
MAYOR
p
Of - fi - cial re - cog -
Vic.
pure,.... vir - tuous life.
sempre pp
ALBERT
mf
Well, I'll be blowed!
May.
- ni - tion of your mo - des - ty!
SUPERINTENDENT
p
What cos - tume will he

MUM
And where will that come from?
FLORENCE
White like a swan!
ALBERT
Me
VICAR
A roy - al crown!
Sup.
wear?
LADY BILLOWS
We'll see to that all right.
Flo.
Bring me his size in
Alb.
dressed in white, oh no!

MUM
Seems ri - di - cu - lous to
Flo.
shoes and hats to - night to give the tai - lor.
LADY BILLOWS
Now, Her - ring, don't be has - ty, don't be has - ty!
Mum
me!
ALBERT
The whole thing's daft!
MISS WORDSWORTH
But of course!
Alb.
MAYOR
Of course, the
VICAR
But be - fore we part should we not men - tion?...
cresc.

87
Miss W.
Of course, the prize, the prize, the prize, the prize, the
FLORENCE
Of course, the prize, of course, the prize, the prize, the prize, the prize, the
May.
prize! The prize! The prize, the prize, the prize, the
Vic.
Of course, the prize, the prize, the
SUPER
Of course, the prize, the prize, the prize, the
87
Miss W.
prize!
LADY BILLOWS f
When this great day ar - rives, Al-bert will re - ceive, ... be-sides his
Flo.
prize!
May.
prize!
Vic.
prize!
Sup.
prize!
f

Ldy.B.
più f
crown, A prize in gol-den coins,– Five and twen-ty pounds, yes, five and twen-ty
poco cresc.
Ldy.B.
pounds!
MUM
più f
Twen-ty-five pounds, all of his own! Twen-ty-five pounds, all of his
sim.
ff
pp
Mum
own! (Al-bert, say Thank you!) as well as a crown?...
cresc.
88 LADY BILLOWS
f
In of-fer-ing this prize, Our aim is to en-
ff

Ldy. B.
fz
più
-sure vir-tue has its just, its just re - ward from
fff
fff
The Committee leaves the shop, followed to the door by Mum.
MISS WORDSWORTH
ff
And so good-bye, Al - bert,— No! Au re-voir!
Ldy. B.
(gl.)
us.. Au re-voir!
FLORENCE
And so good-bye, Al - bert,— No! Au re-voir!
MUM
Good-morning to you all!.....
MAYOR
And so good-bye, Al - bert,— No! Au re-voir!
VICAR
And so good-bye, Al - bert,— No! Au re-voir!
SUPER
And so good-bye, Al - bert,— No! Au re-voir!
8va
sim
mf
sf
f
ff

Mum
Good morning to you all! ....
poco a poco dim.
Good morning to you
Mum turns back into the shop.
all!........
We ll! think of
pp
molto cresc.
89
Moderate but heavy ♩. = 112
(Moderato ma pesante)
ff sempre
that, my lad! Being King of the May and all, And........ the

Mum
en-vy of eve-ry-one, King of the May! King of the May! and
ff
f
dim.
marcatiss.
twen-ty-five quid in ad-di-tion!...
ALBERT
p
But I dont want that kind of po-
always short
(sempre stacc.)
pp
pp
rather heavy (poco pesante)
D.B. (pizz.)
90
You won't ac-cept,— Why e-ver
Alb.
-si-tion, And I don't think I'm going to ac-cept.
90
pp
cresc.
not? You can't............ re-fuse! Not while you live... with
Oh yes, I can!
sim.
sf
p
p
ffz

Mum
Alb.
me, young man, ... you'll do as you're told! Don't "lis-ten" me!
Now lis-ten, Mum!
sim.
poco f
Why should they come and dress me up, like a blink - ing swan? Make
speeches at me like I was stuffed in - stead of flesh and blood!
psim.
MUM
91
Stop shout - ing at me, and
marked
fetch me my tape from the box on the kitchen safe. I'll measure you up! I'll
Oh no, you

truculently
Mum
mea-sure you up! You heard .... what I said!
Alb.
won't! Oh no, you won't! I did, ...
sim.
p
sf p
p heavy (pesante)
Mum
I'll take a
Alb.
.... and don't you think I'm will - ing, ... 'cos........ I'm not!
cresc.
mf
92
sf Mum drives Albert across the shop. He dodges her.
Mum
strap to you, that's what! Young de-vil! ......
Alb.
f
You try it, then!
92
ff

Mum
Alb.
Young de-vil!
You try it, then!
I'm old e - nough to choose for my-
f
sim.
pp
f
I brought you up!
Oh!
- self!
You shut me up in the shop all day!
f
p poco a poco cresc.
cresc. molto
93
sf
seething
pp (soffocato)
The wick-ed in - gra-ti-tude of it!
ff
pp
pp
The wick-ed in - gra-ti-tude of it!
pp
You'll
sf
freely
(ad lib.)
pay for
pp
ppp
with the voice (colla voce)

animating a little (*poco animando*)
Mum
this, my boy!
ALBERT
I'm sick and tired .... of being or-dered a-bout!
animating a little (*poco animando*)
W.W.
express.
pp
Mum gets a grip on Albert and pushes him across to the inner door.
p cresc.
You lit - tle li - ar! You lit - tle li - ar! I won't stand
Alb.
I'm sick and tired ....
94
here and be..... at - tacked by a kid who wants his bot - - - - - tom smacked! Go up to bed, Go up to bed! Shut the
The three kids look in and watch through the shop door.
f
cresc.

Mum shoves Albert through the door and up the stairs.
Mum
door, and don't you dare.......... to come down be-fore you're rea - -
mf
cresc.
f
Very animated ♩. = 132
95
(Molto animato)
(off)
ff
- dy to say........ sor-ry! Go on!
EMMIE, CIS, HARRY
ff
Al - bert's Mum took a stick, Whacked him on the
sff
p
You de-vil! You de-vil!
Em.
Cis
Har.
sf
thing-mi-jig! Al - bert hopped round the shop, Squeak-ing like a

Mum
Em. Cis Har.
ff
I'll teach......... you! ....
til - ly - pig!
Al - bert's Mum took a stick,
sf p
whacked him on the thing - mi - jig!
Go on!........
Al - bert hopped round the shop,
Mum turns back into the shop and slams the door in the faces of the kids, who run off laughing wildly.
squeak - ing like a til - ly - pig!

96
Em.
Cis
Har.
fff
Ha! .... ha! ha! ha! ha! ha! ha! ha! ha! ha! ha! ha! ha!
fff
dim.
pp
MUM p
Twen-ty-five quid!
più f
Twen-ty-five quid!
f
Blood-y lit-tle fool!
ppp
sim.
97 a tempo, fast (presto) She goes off upstairs again.
freely
(ad lib.)
Mum
Bloody lit-tle fool!
p molto cresc.
QUICK CURTAIN
f cresc.
G. P.
fff
sf
End of Act I

ACT II

Scene I

sempre cresc.
1
sfp
Str.
f expr.
cresc. molto

8va
freely
(ad lib.)
p rubato
(rall.)
ff
fff
CURTAIN
The scene is inside a marquee set up in the Vicarage garden. There is a long trestle-table loaded with cakes, jellies and
2
other good things. Nancy is bringing in plates of sandwiches. Florence bustles into the tent, dressed in her best clothes.
Animated recitative
(Recitativo animato)
FLORENCE f
Is-n't he
Piano
p
sim.
NANCY
Not yet.
He prom-ised to come by three.
Flo.
here?
Oh, drat the lad!
I'm as-

Nan.
Don't trou-ble to wait.
Flo.
-to-nished at him, to-day of all days! I should
Nan.
There's on-ly the meat to un-pack and put out on the plates; I can
Flo.
hate to miss them.
Nan.
ea-si-ly do that a-lone.
Flo.
The Vicar es-pe-cial-ly asked me to be there at half-past, to be

more broadly
(più largamente)
Flo.
took in the pho-to-graph group for The Ips-wich and Dis-trict Ga-zette.
Sid arrives outside the tent on his bicycle, and hurries to unload a large box of food.
NANCY
Here he is at last!
Hurry up, Sid!
Flo.
And high time too!
Everything's ready but you!
SID
Am I late?
poco a poco cresc.
Very quick
(Allegro molto)
Flo.
Punctured your bike! Punctured your bike!
For
Sid
Sor-ry, Miss Pike! Punctured my bike!
Very quick
(Allegro molto)

3
Approaching Sid indignantly.
Flo.
three pre - cious weeks we've been toil - ing and scra - ping,
l.h.
p
heavy
(pesante)
Bust - ling, ... hur - ry-ing, Hur - ry-ing, ... scur - ry-ing,
With one aim in sight, ... and
f
now at the e - lev - enth hour you you YOU ....
l.h.
p

Flo.
keep everything wait - ing, be - cause of your
cresc.
ff
4
bike!
I think you're
mf dim.
pp
poco a poco cresc.
la - zy and most re - pre - hen - si - ble! Sure - ly you
sempre cresc.
know that the meat's in - dis - pen - sa - ble? Late - ness on
ffz ff

Nancy tries to interrupt Florence.
5
NANCY
It's twenty past...
Flo.
May-Day is quite in-de-fen-si-ble!
5 Tutti
W.W.
Vc.
ff
pp
Then I must fly, ... or they'll leave me out!
cresc.
Florence hurries off. Sid runs after her and shouts:
SID
You........ bum-ble
cresc. molto
ffz
f (pizz.)
Sid turns and examines the display of food.
Sid
off! that-'ll be much more sen-si-ble!
Vc.
ff dim.
f

a little slower
(poco più lento)
NANCY
Don't you think it's a splen-did sur-prise?
Sid
f
That's... a fine sight for sore eyes!
p
And they
pp
Str.
f
fpp
Nan.
Sid
make all this fuss, 'cos Al-bert's too shy to go out on a bust!
p
What were things
p
like down there in the town?
muted Hn.
p freely (ad lib.)
rubato
f
Slow and dignified ♩= 56
(Lento con dignità)
6
parlante e sempre liberamente (always freely)
SID p
Churchyard's a - gog with a crowd of folk who could - n't get in for the

Sid
ser-vice. Seats have been kept for the Band of Hope, and each choir
Tutti
ppp sust., expr.
.... boy has got a new sur-plice. The Vi-car is preach-ing on
fpp
'Liv - ing Chaste For the Here - af - - - - - - ter.'
pp
fpp
ppp
rather heavy
(poco pesante)
light
(leggiero)
pp
Some of his listeners are so-lemn-faced,.... Some near to.... laugh - ter.
fp
fp
ppp

7 animating
(animando)
uneasily cresc.
p (inquieto)
Sid
And Al - bert! sit - ting there in his pew,
pp
Timp.
poco marc.
The poor kid looks on ten - ter-hooks. He's in the
sempre più f
poco a poco cresc.
mood to es-cape if he could:–
slower
(più lento)
ppp
I'd like to see him go for
fz
pp
good!
muted Hn.
p
rubato
pp cresc.
f

Animated recitative
(*Recitativo animato*)

They lift the box of food between them and go off.

Miss W.
- fore they........come!
9
EMMIE (whispering)
Bli - mey! Jel - ly!
CIS (whispering)
Pink blancmange!
9
Miss W.
Placing them in line
All stand
Em.
With i - cing on!..........
Cis
With i - cing on!..........
HARRY (whispering)
Seedy cake! Seed-y cake! With i - cing on! ....
Miss W.
neat - ly....... in a row, head back! fin-gers so!

Miss W.
One deep breath........... and off.................
.... we go!
10
CIS f (whispering)
Sausa-gey rolls!
HARRY f (whispering)
Trea - cle tart!
dim.
pp
EMMIE f (whispering)
Tri - fle! Tri - fle! In a big bowl!.....
Cis
In a big bowl!.....
Har.
In a big bowl!.....
sf
Food comes

Miss W.
la - ter. First we sing— GLO - RY TO OUR NEW MAY
KING! — Try to make the wel - kin ring! At-ten-tion now!
f
più f
8
cresc.
Miss Wordsworth sounds her pitch-pipe.
11
No fid-get-ing.
[PIPE]
ff
She beats one.
There is Doh!
[PIPE]
One and two and...
f

Miss W.
with force (con forza)
No! .... When I reach two you have to be a-
-gog to start on the beat of three!
12
EMMIE
Chic-ken and ham!
CIS
Cheesey straws!
12
Miss Wordsworth sounds her pipe again.
[PIPE]
One and two and...
with force (con forza)
CIS & EMMIE
GLO - RY TO OUR NEW MAY
HARRY
And marzi-pan!
with force (con forza)
GLO - RY TO OUR NEW MAY
cresc.
W.W.

13
(♩. = preceding ♩)
Miss W.
O, O........ what a noise, O........ what a noise!
Em. Cis
KING!..................
Har.
KING!..................
pp
That's much.... too shrill, and Har-ry, You should just
Miss Wordsworth sounds pipe.
try to keep still!....................
[PIPE] One and two and...
(♩. = ♩)
14
Not "'AIL," my dears, not
f EMMIE, CIS & HARRY
GLO - RY TO OUR NEW MAY KING! AL-BERT 'AIL! ALL...
W.W.
p

Miss W.
"'AIL," my dears! The word is HAIL!
A clean, crisp note from an o - pen throat.
HAIL!.. In - sert.... your ait - ches in their pro - per
pla - ces.
15
ALBERT, HAIL! ALL HAIL! WE SING...

Miss W.
Em. Cis Har.
(♩ = ♩.)
Too... many now, but that must do, Try the next lines
HAL-BERT, HAIL! HALL HAIL!
16
Fer-vent-ly through... Sing with fire! Be-gin-ning on Fah. You, Emmie, higher...
Your note is Lah. Doh, ray, mi, FAH, soh, LAH!
Harp
Str.
17
Miss Wordsworth beats time as they sing.
(♩ = preceding ♩.)
Doh, ray, mi, FAH, soh, LAH.
EMMIE
EACH SIN-GLE VOICE CRIES
CIS
EACH SIN-GLE
Fl.

Em.
OUT RE - JOICE! IN HAP-PY SONG BOTH LOUD...
Cis
VOICE CRIES OUT RE - JOICE! IN HAP-PY SONG BOTH LOUD...
Har.
ff desperate (disperato)
EACH SINGLE VOICE CRIES... IN HAPPY SONG BOTH LOUD...
MISS WORDSWORTH
O Har-ry! This is where you al - ways go wrong! Just fol-low Cis, she'll help you a-long!
dim.
Miss W.
Harry raises his hand urgently.
G.P.
18
Miss Wordsworth signals Harry to go. He runs out, followed by the girls.
Don't take too long! Our song must be -
HARRY
Please, tea-cher..?
pp

She follows the children out.
Miss W.
-gin Ex-act-ly on their co-ming...... in!
sempre pp
Sid and Nancy come in cautiously, carrying jugs of lemonade.
Recit.
NANCY (apprehensive)
pp
I don't think you ought!
SID pp
Stop spoil-ing the fun! Is this where he's sit-ting?
Piano
pp
Sid takes the glass from Albert's place, and a hip-flask from his pocket.
Nan.
The right-hand-ed one!
Sid
pp
Then you be-gin fil-ling the
pp

poco a poco accel.
cresc.
Nan.
Don't give him too much! He
Sid
glass-es all up, while I add a drop to His Majesty's cup.
poco a poco accel.
cresc.
He pours some rum into the glass.
Nan.
mustn't get tight.
più f
Sid
Just loosen him up and make him feel bright.
pp
I
Vla. (p) express.
ff
Nancy fills the glass with lemonade.
Nan.
pp
It's much the same shade —
Sid
think that's all right. Now add lemon - ade —

slower
(più lento)
Nan.
pp
Ex-cept-ing for Al-bert,
Sid
pp
Now no-one can smell there's rum in as well,
slower
(più lento)
pp sweetly
(dolce)
Nancy sees the procession approaching.
19
Majestic
(Maestoso)
Nan.
And he'll ne-ver tell!
f
Quick, here they are! Fill up the
Sid
And he'll ne-ver tell!
19
Majestic
(Maestoso)
w.w.
mf
Bells
f
They quickly put Albert's glass back in its place and fill all the others with lemonade.
Nan.
rest.
Sid
f
We'll stand at the side —
f
ff
Str.

Miss Wordsworth hurries the children in again, each carrying a bunch of flowers.

21
MUM
f
marked
Yes, ... he does look a treat, in his white
Sup.
son, Missus Herring!
21
f
mf
Mum
suit........ I could-n't help feel-ing proud of him too.
The Mayor arrives with Florence.
Majestic
(Maestoso)
pp
f Bells
FLORENCE
f
Quicker (Più mosso)
marcatiss.
For three weeks at
MAYOR
f
To-day's a big af-fair for you, Miss Pike!
Quicker (Più mosso)
l.h.
fp
p
p
f
Majestic
(Maestoso)
Flo.
least we've been plan - ning this feast, your Wor-ship!
cresc.
f

 The Vicar arrives with Lady Billows.

* This B♭ can be obtained by over-blowing the A pipe (used previously).

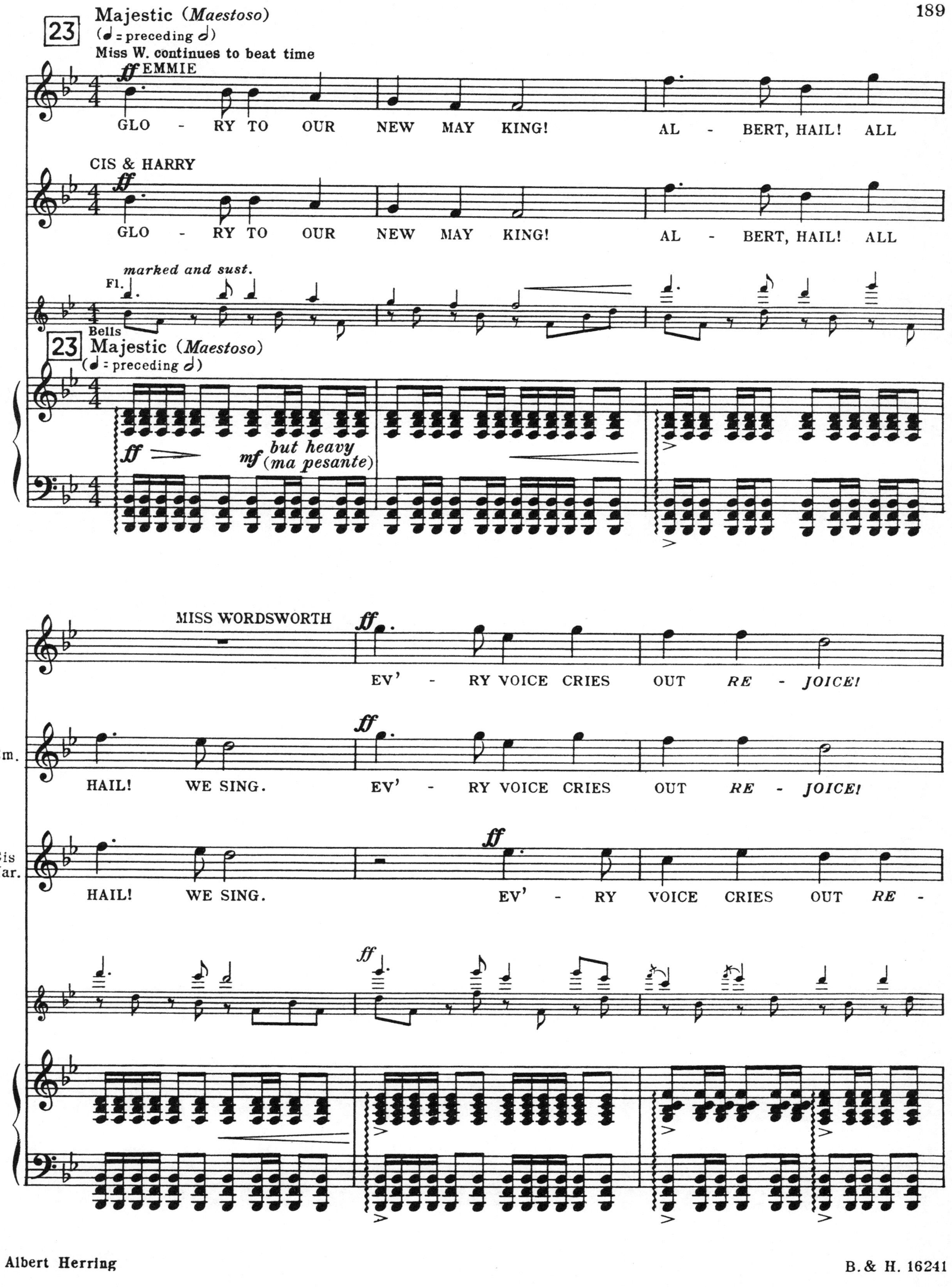
23
Majestic (Maestoso)
(♩ = preceding 𝅗𝅥)
Miss W. continues to beat time
ff EMMIE
GLO - RY TO OUR NEW MAY KING! AL - BERT, HAIL! ALL
CIS & HARRY
ff
GLO - RY TO OUR NEW MAY KING! AL - BERT, HAIL! ALL
marked and sust.
Fl.
Bells
23
Majestic (Maestoso)
(♩ = preceding 𝅗𝅥)
ff
mf but heavy (ma pesante)
MISS WORDSWORTH
ff
EV' - RY VOICE CRIES OUT RE - JOICE!
Em.
HAIL! WE SING.
ff
EV' - RY VOICE CRIES OUT RE - JOICE!
Cis Har.
HAIL! WE SING.
ff
EV' - RY VOICE CRIES OUT RE -
ff

Miss W.
IN HAP-PY SONG BOTH LOUD AND LONG!
Em.
IN HAP-PY SONG BOTH LOUD AND LONG! HAIL! AL-BERT, AL -
Cis Har.
-JOICE! IN HAP-PY SONG BOTH LOUD AND LONG! HAIL! AL-BERT, AL -
ff mf
Em.
- BERT! WE CRY. WEL - COME TO YOUR MA - JES - TY!
Cis Har.
- BERT! WE CRY. WEL - COME TO YOUR MA - JES - TY!

Em.
HAIL! AL - BERT! HAIL! WE CRY. WEL - COME TO............ YOUR
Cis Har.
HAIL! AL - BERT! HAIL! WE CRY. WEL - COME TO........... YOUR
cresc.
Everyone applauds enthusiastically, breaking out into conversation.
MISS WORDSWORTH
HAIL!!
Em.
MA - JES - TY. HAIL!!
Cis Har.
MA - JES - TY. HAIL!!

*) This Recitative Ensemble is not to be sung in time. Each character sings his line at the natural speed of the diction, repeating it until interrupted by the *ff* chord.

Har.
few And ten-der my years But these are for you Who Loxford re -
D.B. (pizz.)
sf roughly (ruvido)
sf
sf
He shoves the flowers at Lady Billows.
Much applause.
MISS WORDSWORTH
Emmie kneels
ff
Emmie Spashett!
sf
Har.
-veres.
cresc.
ffzpp
ffz
sf
sf
in front of Albert, to his great confusion.
25
Quick (Allegro)
EMMIE
neatly (netto)
very short (staccatissimo)
Sim-ple song, Coun-try flowers, Wish you
Fl.
pp
Ob.
Applause as Emmie gives Albert the flowers.
MISS WORDSWORTH
f
Now, Cissie Woodger!
Em.
long And hap-py hours.
ffzpp
ff

Cissie is shy, and has to be propelled forwards to give her flowers to Mrs Herring.

Mum steps forward and takes the flowers from Cis, who runs away in tears.
Miss W.
"'Twas yours to dis..."
Cis
-ray, hoo-ray, hoo-ray...
Boo! hoo! hoo! hoo! hoo! hoo! hoo!
MUM
Well done, dea-rie!
sfp
LADY BILLOWS
Thank you, chil-dren! And thank you......... Miss
Mum
Ve-ry nice, I'm sure!
poco a poco cresc.
All move to the table. They chat as they find their places and sit.
27
Majestic as before
(Maestoso come sopra)
Ldy. B.
Wordsworth!
Come, let's sit down.
ff

*) See footnote on p. 192

The vicar rises.

She rises ponderously.
Broadly
(Largamente) 𝅗𝅥 = 60
Ldy. B.
I'm full of hap-pi-ness To be here in your midst On such...... a day as this,
sonorous
As honoured guest and pa - tro-ness
stringendo
Of the Lox-ford Ur-ban
Dis-trict May - - Day Feast.
28
Enthusiastic applause.
sim.
She silences the clapping.
LADY BILLOWS
Seat - ed.... up-on my right is Al-bert Her-ring
express.

Ldy. B.
cresc.
dim.
A young man chosen, marked out, set a-part—
For honest worth and pu-ri-ty of
w.w.
cresc.
ff
p
pp
heart. You see that in the costume he is wearing —
Virgin white and orange blossom crown.
pp
ppp
29
pp
with warmth
(con calore)
Dear chil-dren! You, you, the rising gene-ra-tion!
w.w.
pp
cresc.
with ped.
Ne-ver for-get the meaning of this day! Trea-sure its ex-am-ple!
pp

Ldy. B.
pp
Think,.... oh think .... of Al-bert! Scorn the sweetmeats of temp-
p dim.
pp
gradually becoming more urgent
(poco a poco incalzando)
-ta-tion, Se-duc-ing you from straight and narrow ways — Carnal in-dul-gence!
gradually becoming more urgent
(poco a poco incalzando)
Gambling! — Playing cards! — Ir-re-lig-ion!..... Pa-triotism is not e-nough! — and
30
fz
DRINK!.. The havoc wrought by gin!
p cresc.
Oh, ne-ver start that
ffp

Ldy. B.
dread - ful ha-bit, or you're lost for - e - - ver!
cresc. molto
She has dropped her notes.
King and Coun-try.....! Clean - li-ness is next to.....!
Hn.
Str.
God for England and Saint.....! Keep your powder dry...........
31 very animated (animato molto)
.... and leave the rest to Na - ture....! Bri - tons!
FLORENCE
Hoo -
MAYOR
Hoo-ray! Hoo -
31 very animated (animato molto)

MISS WORDSWORTH
f
Hoo-ray!
Hoo -
Ldy.B.
Rule ....
the
deep,
Rule ....
the
EMMIE CIS & HARRY
f
Hoo-ray!
NANCY
f
Hoo - ray!
MUM
f
Hoo-ray!
Flo.
- ray!
Hoo -
May.
- ray!
Hoo - ray!
SID
f
Hoo-ray!
VICAR
f
Hoo-ray!
SUPERINTENDENT
f
Hoo-ray!
Hoo -
ff
5
4
f
ff
5
f
6
7

Miss W.
- ray! Hoo - ray! Hoo - ray! Hoo - ray!
Ldy. B.
deep, Rule!
Em. Cis. Har.
Hoo - ray! Hoo - ray!
Nan.
Hoo - ray!
Mum
Hoo - ray! Hoo - ray! Hoo - ray!
Flo.
- ray! Hoo - ray! Hoo - ray! Hoo - ray!
May.
Hoo - ray! Hoo - ray! Hoo - ray!
Sid
Hoo - ray!
Vic.
Hoo - ray! Hoo - ray! Hoo - ray!
Sup.
- ray! Hoo - ray! Hoo - ray! Hoo - ray!
ff
f

f marcatiss.
Ldy. B.
Albert, arise! Stand to receive this purse of otter skin,— My father shot the brute in 'Fifty-six on Christmas Eve,—With five-and-twenty sovereigns inside!
ffz
f
Take it, my boy, take it with joyful pride!
pp
B. D.
stringendo
All this is yours, and you deserve the lot.
poco cresc.
molto cresc.
32
Great applause as Albert takes the purse and raises his hat. Lady Billows sits and
ff

the vicar rises again.
Recit. (broadly)
(largamente)
VICAR
Mag-ni - fi-cent, your La-dy-ship! Our best thanks to
Vic.
you! A splendid speech, a splendid prize and splendid-ly de-served! .... Now,
, f sempre
Piano
f
rall.
Mis-ter Mayor, will you please rise and add an-o-ther word?
The Mayor stands up.
p
pp
Very quick ♩= 184
(Allegro molto)
MAYOR (reading)
f automatic
"As re-pre-sent-ing....... our lo-cal coun-cil, I'm
Str. f
May.
ve-ry hap-py.... to de-clare our-selves in full a-gree-ment .... with her

with expression
(con espress.)
as before
f (come sopra)
May.
La - - dy-ship, Thank-ing her most hear-ty,...... hear-ti-
pp
f
May.
-ly, for the i-deal She sets our town..... in mo-ral
with expression
(con espress.)
lead - - er-
p
meno f
May.
ship. The re-per-cus-sions of this Fes-ti-val will tra-vel far, wide, deep...
p
più f
May.
......and strong, Like when my Coun-cil, act-ing for the best of all its ci-ti-zens,
poco a poco cresc.
più f
May.
laid the 12-inch wa-ter main, Cost-ing six pounds ten the yard, that runs a-long thro' Ba-la-cla-va
sempre cresc.
sempre cresc.

May.
A - ven - ue Re-gard-less of ob - jec-tions, to guar-an-tee pure wa - ter fil-tered
triumphantly
(con trionfo)
ff
from .... in - fec-tions!
sf
(deep breath.)
f
Now Lox-ford leads a-gain by be - ing
sfp
f
mf
first, yes! First in crown-ing a May King. "Well done!".......... I hear you
expr.
p
cry. — "Well done!"............ I hear you cry. — "Well
più f
33
VICAR
f
Well
ff

MISS WORDSWORTH
Well done! .... We...
LADY BILLOWS
Well done! .... We...
EMMIE & CIS
Well done! .... We...
HARRY
Well done! .... We...
NANCY
Well done! .... We...
MUM
Well done! .... We...
FLORENCE
Well done! .... We...
MAYOR
done!"
My Coun-cil wishes me to mark to-
SID
Well done! .... We...
VICAR
done! .... We...
SUPERINTENDENT
Well done! .... We...
p cresc.
ff

May.
- day By of-fer-ing this prize to Al-bert, which they have vo-ted from the Entertainment
f
f
May.
Fund — This Savings Book in which he'll find .... five pounds.
sweetly (dolce)
34
Applause, as
p
ff
he hands Albert the savings book.
Recit.
VICAR f
Fas-ci-na-ting, Mister Mayor, a fitting gift in-deed to
Piano f
Vic.
cresc.
store a-way for a rai-ny day and keep in case of need. And now, Miss
p
mf
f
dim.
p
Emmie, who had left the table, reappears with two large books which she places before Miss Wordsworth.
Vic.
dim.
pp
Words-worth... you will not dis-ap-point us? Oh! You have a sur-prise, I
p
pp

35
Gently moving ♩. = 56
(Andante con moto)
Miss Wordsworth rises.
Vic.
see!
Fl.
tr
pp
Harp
Clt.
quasi gliss.
MISS WORDSWORTH
f
My.... heart leaps up with
cresc.
Miss W.
joy to see vir - tue and sim -
dim.
- pli - ci - ty, Ap - plaud - ed, re - ward - ed and....
cresc.

Miss W.
glo - ri - fied with heart - felt warmth on....
tr
tr
Miss W.
ev' - ry side!
tr
ff
3
3
Miss W.
p
Al - bert!
tr
dim.
tr
Miss W.
Al - bert!........... the teach - ers...
tr
tr

clearly
p (distinto)
Miss W.
from the school, Miss Podd, Miss Tut-tle, dear Miss Butler and Miss Toole, Are
tr
pp
ppp
cresc.
proud of you, proud of you, as I am too, and pro-
3
cresc.
-found - ly stirred by.... your re - nown.
f
Al - bert! Al - bert! Al - bert!

36
She takes up the books.
Miss W.
p parlante
They
ff
dim.
send this lit-tle gift to you For rai-ny af-ter-noons — 'FOXE'S BOOK OF MAR - TYRS' —
f
Harp p simply (semplice)
Gong
8va
p
In two fine vol-umes, il-lus-tra-ted, — in - scribed to you ap-propriately and
Applause as Albert receives the books from Miss Wordsworth.
dat-ed.
VICAR p
The Bi-ble, Shakespeare,
tr
gliss on black keys
w.
ff
dim.
pp

Recit.
heavier
(più pesante)
Vic.
Fox-e's Book of Mar-tyrs — Three cor-ner-stones of our na-tion-al
pp Gong
Piano
p
8va
beginning slowly and animating
(cominciando lento ed animando)
he-ri-tage! Thank you, ... Miss Wordsworth, very much. To
mf
dim.
pp
smooth
(legato e) molto cresc.
make our thanks complete, one voice is miss-ing, ... Yes, Mister Budd's, — Last but hardly
ff
37
Moderate but with spirit ♩= 104
(Moderato ma con anima)
The Superintendent rises.
least!
SUPERINTENDENT
Er-humph! Er-humph! I'm no.... great shakes as a
D.B.
sempre f e marcato

Sup.
speechi-fi-er,
But my heart's warm e-nough, if you know what I mean! _
It's
chaps like young Al - bert keep the Bri-tish Em - pire on top of the world,
Where it has al-ways been.
38
Good old Al-bert! Good old
ff
p
mf
p
sempre molto f
Al-bert! That's my o-pin-ion...
cresc.
Good luck, good luck, good luck to
mf
pp
cresc.
meno f e cresc.

He sits among applause and half rises again.
ff
Sup.
you .... my boy! Er-humph! Er-humph! Be-fore I wind up,
quasi trillo
f
dim.
ff
p parlando
I mus-n't for-get to thank Missus Wil-liams for the loan of her flag-pole
p light but clear (leggiero ma distinto)
Recit.
VICAR
f
Thank you! Thank you! Now_ I'm
and two do-zen cups.
f
p
gliss.
Piano
f
Vic.
p
cer-tain Al-bert feels the need of speak-ing in his turn_ Re-
p

Vic.
cresc.
f
pp
- turn-ing thanks for gifts received, Be - fore the feast's be - gun?
cresc.
(♩. = ♩)
f
p
Albert rises slowly and miserably.
39
Very moderate 𝅗𝅥 = 50
(Molto moderato)
Bells
pp
Vla.
Vc.
Vlns.
express.
tr
3
The others encourage him to speak, but Albert hesitates.
MUM pp
Go on, Al-bert!
FLORENCE pp
Say 'thank you!'
VICAR pp
Don't be shy!
Harp
pp
Bells
pp
express. cresc.
tr
sf
3

MISS WORDSWORTH
p
Say a word or two!
LADY BILLOWS
f
Come a-long now!
NANCY
Poor Al-bert!
MAYOR
mf
It's just po-lite!
SID
pp
Poor Al-bert!
SUPERINTENDENT
p
Don't be scared, old boy.
pp
Albert pulls himself together as if to speak
Bells
40
pp
express.
cresc. molto
- but loses his nerve
- then tries again.
ALBERT
p
Er...
f passionate
(appass.)
dim.

He sits abruptly.
Alb.
Er...
Thank you - - - - - - - - - ve-ry much!
Bells
ppp
p
Harp
pp
ff
41
Lively (Vivace)
MISS WORDSWORTH & LADY BILLOWS
Oh, Al - bert!
Poor Al - bert!
EMMIE & CIS
Al - bert!
HARRY
Al - bert!
NANCY & MUM
Al - bert!
FLORENCE
Oh, Al - bert!
Poor Al - bert!
MAYOR
Oh, Al - bert!
Poor Al - bert!
SID
Al - bert!
SUPERINTENDENT
Oh, Al - bert!
Poor Al - bert!
41
Lively (Vivace)
ff

Miss W. Ldy.B.
Bit short, was-n't it?............
Em. Cis
Al - bert! That did-n't take long!.....
Har.
Al - bert! That did-n't take long!....
Nan. Mum
Al - bert! That did-n't take long!....
Flo.
Bit short, was-n't it?............
May.
Bit short, was-n't it?............
Sid
Al - bert! That did-n't take long!....
Sup.
Bit short, was-n't it?............

42
Miss W. Ldy.B.
Try a - gain! Bet - ter luck next time!
Em. Cis
Try a - gain! Try a -
Har.
Try a - gain! Try a -
Nan. Mum
Try a - gain! Try a -
Flo.
Try a - gain! Bet - ter luck next time!
May.
Try a - gain! Bet - ter luck next time!
Sid
Try a - gain! Try a -
Sup.
Try a - gain! Bet - ter luck next time!
42
cresc.

Miss W. Ldy. B.
ff
Short and sweet! That did-n't take long!........ He's scar'd, poor Al - bert!...
Em. Cis
ff
-gain! He's scar'd! That did-n't take long!.... Short and
Har.
ff
-gain! He's scar'd! That did-n't take long!.... Short and
Nan. Mum
ff
-gain! He's scar'd! That did-n't take long!.... Short and
Flo.
ff
Short and sweet! That did-n't take long!........ He's scar'd, poor Al - bert!...
May.
ff
Short and sweet! That did-n't take long!........ He's scar'd, poor Al - bert!...
Sid
ff
-gain! He's scar'd! That did-n't take long!.... Short and
Sup.
ff
Short and sweet! That did-n't take long!........ He's scar'd, poor Al - bert!...
ff

The vicar stops them.

Vic.
-trays a heart too full to prate or boast. Now lift your glass-es,
f marked
sfp
everyone........ and join me in a toast! ....
All stand.
sf
sf
ff
43
broadly
f (largamente)
Al - bert the Good! Long may he reign! To be
marked
w p sust.
f Str.
p
f
p
re - e - lect - ed a - gain.... and a - gain!
f

44
MISS WORDSWORTH & LADY BILLOWS
ff sust.
Al - bert the Good! Long may he reign! To be
EMMIE & CIS
ff sust.
Al - bert the Good! Long may he reign! To be
HARRY
ff sust.
Al - bert the Good! Long may he reign! To be
NANCY
ff sust.
Al - bert the Good! Long may he reign! To be
MUM
ff sust.
Al - bert the Good! Long may he reign! To be
FLORENCE
ff sust.
Al - bert the Good! Long may he reign! To be
MAYOR
ff sust.
Al - bert the Good! Long may he reign! To be
SID
ff sust.
Al - bert the Good! Long may he reign! To be
Vic.
ff sust.
Al - bert the Good! Long may he reign! To be
SUPERINTENDENT
ff sust.
Al - bert the Good! Long may he reign! To be
44
ff sust.

Miss W. Ldy. B.
re-e-lect-ed a-gain........ and a-gain, ... and a-
Em. Cis
re-e-lect-ed a-gain and a-gain, and a-gain, ...
Har.
re-e-lect-ed a-gain and a-gain, and a-gain, ...
Nan.
re-e-lect-ed a-gain and a-gain, and a-gain, ...
Mum
re-e-lect-ed a-gain and a-gain, and a-gain, ...
Flo.
re-e-lect-ed a-gain........ and a-gain, ... and a-
May.
re-e-lect-ed a-gain and a-gain, and a-gain, ...
Sid
re-e-lect-ed a-gain........ and a-gain, ... and a-
Vic.
re-e-lect-ed a-gain........ and a-gain, ... and a-
Sup.
re-e-lect-ed a-gain and a-gain, and a-gain, ...

Miss W. Ldy.B.
-gain, and a - gain, and a - gain,
Em. Cis
and a - gain, and a - gain, and a -
Har.
and a - gain, and a - gain, and a -
Nan.
and a - gain, and a - gain, and a -
Mum
and a - gain, and a - gain, and a -
Flo.
-gain, and a - gain, and a - gain,
May.
and a - gain, and a - gain, and a -
Sid
-gain, and a - gain, and a - gain,
Vic.
-gain, and a - gain, and a - gain,
Sup.
and a - gain, and a - gain, and a -
cresc.

45
Miss W.
and a-gain! Hoo-
Ldy. B.
and a-gain!
Em. Cis
-gain, and a-gain! Hoo-
Har.
-gain, and a-gain! Hoo-
Nan.
-gain, and a-gain! Hoo-
Mum
-gain, and a-gain! Hoo-
Flo.
and a-gain! Go on, Al-bert! Hoo-
ALBERT
And three cheers for her Ladyship! Hip, hip, hoo-
May.
-gain, and a-gain! Hoo-
Sid
and a-gain! Hoo-
Vic.
and a-gain! Hoo-
Sup.
-gain, and a-gain! Hoo-
45

Miss W.
-ray! Hoo - ray! Hoo-
Em. Cis
-ray! Hoo - ray! Hoo-
Har.
-ray! Hoo - ray! Hoo-
Nan.
-ray! Hoo - ray! Hoo-
Mum
-ray! Hoo - ray! Hoo-
Flo.
-ray! Hoo - ray! Hoo-
Alb.
-ray! Hip, hip, hoo - ray! Hip, hip, hoo-
May.
-ray! Hoo - ray! Hoo-
Sid
-ray! Hoo - ray! Hoo-
Vic.
-ray! Hoo - ray! Hoo-
Sup.
-ray! Hoo - ray! Hoo-
fff
sf
p

Albert lifts his glass, takes a long drink, then another, and drains it entirely.
46
Miss W.
Em. Cis
Har.
Nan.
Mum
Flo.
Alb.
May.
Sid
Vic.
Sup.
sf
- ray!
sempre espress.
W.
sff
f
5
6
3

He moves forward to Nancy to have the glass
refilled.
ALBERT f
That's bet - ter! Thirs - ty!...
(sempre ff)
A hiccup interupts him.
Animated recitative (in tempo)
(Recitativo animato (in tempo))
LADY BILLOWS f
Shall I pat your back?
EMMIE & CIS pp
Wil-lups!
pp (laughing)
Tee! hee! hee! hee! hee! hee! hee!
HARRY pp
Albert's got willups!
pp (laughing)
Tee! hee! hee! hee! hee! hee! hee!
MUM p
Hiccups!
Alb.
More, please!
HIC!
Animated recitative (in tempo)
(Recitativo animato (in tempo))
ffz

All surround Albert, anxious to help.

NANCY pp
Do you think it's the rum?.....
Alb.
mf
It's al-most gone... HIC!
HIC!
SID pp
It's got a
f
f
Nan.
pp
Oh, what have we done?
Alb.
f
Please don't both... HIC!
f
Wate... HIC!
Sid.
kick like a gun!
pp
It was on-ly in fun!
f
f

A glass of lemonade is brought. -
MISS WORDSWORTH
Slow
(Adagio)
Le-mon - ade!
MUM
Lemon-ade!
FLORENCE
From the wrong side!
Alb.
HIC! HIC!
MAYOR
Lemon-ade!
VICAR
Lemon-ade!
SUPERINTENDENT
Lemon - ade!
Slow
(Adagio)
sfpp
con Ped.

Albert bends double to sip from the wrong side of the glass.
Miss W.
p
Drop by drop.
LADY BILLOWS
p
Sip it!
EMMIE CIS & HARRY
He'll go off pop!
Mum
p
Slow-ly!
Vic.
p
Slow-ly!
poco a poco cresc.
He straightens up.
Miss W.
Oh,...... well done!........
Ldy.B.
f
Well then, let's be-
Mum
Bet-ter, son?
(nods)
Alb.
mm!
Vic.
None too soon!
ffz

Everyone sits cheerfully at the table and the feast begins.

*) From here the characters sing again without regard of time at the natural speed of their diction, yet Nancy and Sid, and the Mayor and the Superintendent have two little duets of their own. Also, the children sing the canon at their own time. The tempo indication refers to the orchestra only.

Voices continue
Miss W.
mer-ry! Sit still and be good, dear. There's a moun - tain of food here.
Ldy.B.
books. Here's a plate of sliced ham, You can tuck in to that.
Em. Cis Har.
rumb-ling! Don't 'arf .... keep you wait-ing!
Mum
Ex - cuse me for stretching! Yes, I seem to have two! I
Flo.
If you help in that way, we shall all get served quicker!
Alb.
O, how luck-y I am! Shall I take off my hat?
Vic.
I'd say! A mag - ni - fi-cent spread. Will the children take bread?
Nan.
down! Com - ing now. This is yours!
Sid
Will that do? Plen - ty more. Bring the
May.
f
My!....... does that ham look good!
Sup.
lashings of food! Be-gin-ning with

until the curtain falls and cuts off the hubbub of conversation.

(ff)
48
ff express.
heavy
(pesante)
ff
sf
ff
ff
sim.

49
fff
express.
50
Bsn.
ff dim.
ff
dim.
p
Str.
Cl. pp
pp
cresc.
W.
f
51
ff
Cymb.
ff
ff
pizz.
Ob.
ff
dim.
p
mf

cresc.
52
f
ff
sf
marked
ff
Fl.
53
express.
ff
ff
sf

54
più f
55
smooth
W.W. (legato)
f
Harp
Str.
Fl.
sfp
p marked
dim.
p
56
Cl.
Bsn.
p
pp
Vc.
express.

Hn.
f sempre marc.
sonorous
Timp.
pp poco a poco cresc.
57
f
sempre cresc.
cresc.
f
cresc.
58
ff cresc.
W.W.
fff
Str.
ff
8va
Gong

Bsn.
f
poco a poco dim.
dim.
59
Ob.
p sweetly and gracefully
(dolce e grazioso)
Str.
dim.
2 Vln.
pp
D.B.
Vc.
pp
pp
Vc.
Vla.
D.B.

poco a poco rall.
sempre pp
(rall.)
più rall.
Very much slower
(Molto più lento)
ppp
Bass Clt.
more express.
(più espress.)
sempre rall.
Alto Fl.
60
Slow and quiet ♪=76
(Lento e tranquillo)
pp but very expressive (ma molto espress.)
B.Cl.
very smooth
(legatiss.)

(rubato)
dim.
61
pp

CURTAIN
Inside the shop, later that evening _ Dusk has fallen and light streams through the window from the street lamp outside.
62
more express.
(più espress.)
Str.
Harp
expr.
pp
ppp
pp
Entering gaily, and punctuating his song by banging the shop door and ringing the bell.
63
As before
(Come sopra)
ALBERT
f
Al - bert the Good!........................ Long may he
Shop Bell
sfpp
Alb.
poco a poco accel.
reign. .... To be re - e - lec - ted, and re - se - lec -

Alb.
-ted, and re-ex-pec - ted, And re-sur-rec - ted a-gain..... and a-gain.....
Shop Bell
Str. sfpp
64
He comes into the shop and shouts—
and a-gain and a-gain and again, again, again, a-gain—
cresc.
a tempo
ff
MUM! .... MUM! ....
falsetto
Yoo-hoo!
sf
ffz
p
Harp
pp
65
rhythmic (ritmico)
It's your lit-tle Al-bert, Your su-gar plum Of a pro-di-gal son,
marked
Hrn. Vc.

Alb.
Clean as a whis - tle, Sound as a drum, From his Co - ro - na - ti - um!
p cresc.
ff heavy (pesante)
He shouts again.
He shouts again.
ff
molto rall.
MUM! ....
Stu-pid! Stu-pid!
Ob.
ff
pp
66
Rather quick (Allegretto)
simply (semplice)
a little animated (poco animato)
She's gone to call on Aunt Eth .... For a cup of tea and a chat:
Str.
pp
più f
Left me com - ing straight home to bed, But I'm
più f
f

lively
(vivace)
relaxing
(rilassando)
dim.
Alb.
blowed if I'm rea-dy for that!
I'm blowed........ if I'm rea-dy for
f
f
più p
that!
più rall.
Dark in here!
Must find a match —
f
p dim.
Vc.
67
Albert begins searching round the shop for a box of matches.
And af - ter that we'll light the gas, With en -
A. Fl.
ppp cresc.
f dim.
B. Cl.
Slow as before
(Lento come sopra)
- or - mous care.... not to break the man-tle, Set fire to the shop
pp sempre
B Cl.

Alb.
or cause a scandal!
Matches?...
Matches! Matches!
pp
68
calling
sweetly
p
(dolce)
Swan Ves - tas!
Swan
He finds the matches, goes to the gas bracket and fiddles with it.
molto accel.
Ves - tas!......... Ah!
That's the chap_
molto accel.
cresc. molto
69
more movement
(più mosso)
Turn the tap!
Strike the match like
Str.
fpp
poco f
e con forza

He drops the matches and stoops to pick them up.
Alb.
this —
O drat! Butter fingers!
Oop-sa-dai-sy!
O-pen your mouth, Shut your eyes, Strike the match, For a nice sur-
- prise —
molto cresc.
70
There is a loud BANG! and swoosh of flame from the gas jet.
Albert recoils.
Blast! Dangerous stuff, gas! Smelly, tricky, noi-sy, dangerous stuff!
B.Cl.

He turns the gas hurriedly off.
rall.
71 quietly, as before (tranquillo (come sopra))
Alb.
Leave well a-lone!
A.Fl.
p dim.
pp
espr.
Loosening his belt and relaxing comfortably.
cheerfully (giocoso)
Phew! ....
it's hot!
Belt's too tight for tum.
B.Cl.
singing (cantabile)
Loosen it out a notch:
Relieve my poor... old
ab-do-mum.
Golly! What a party! What a party!
Talk of eating
Hn. muted
ppp
cresc.
sim.

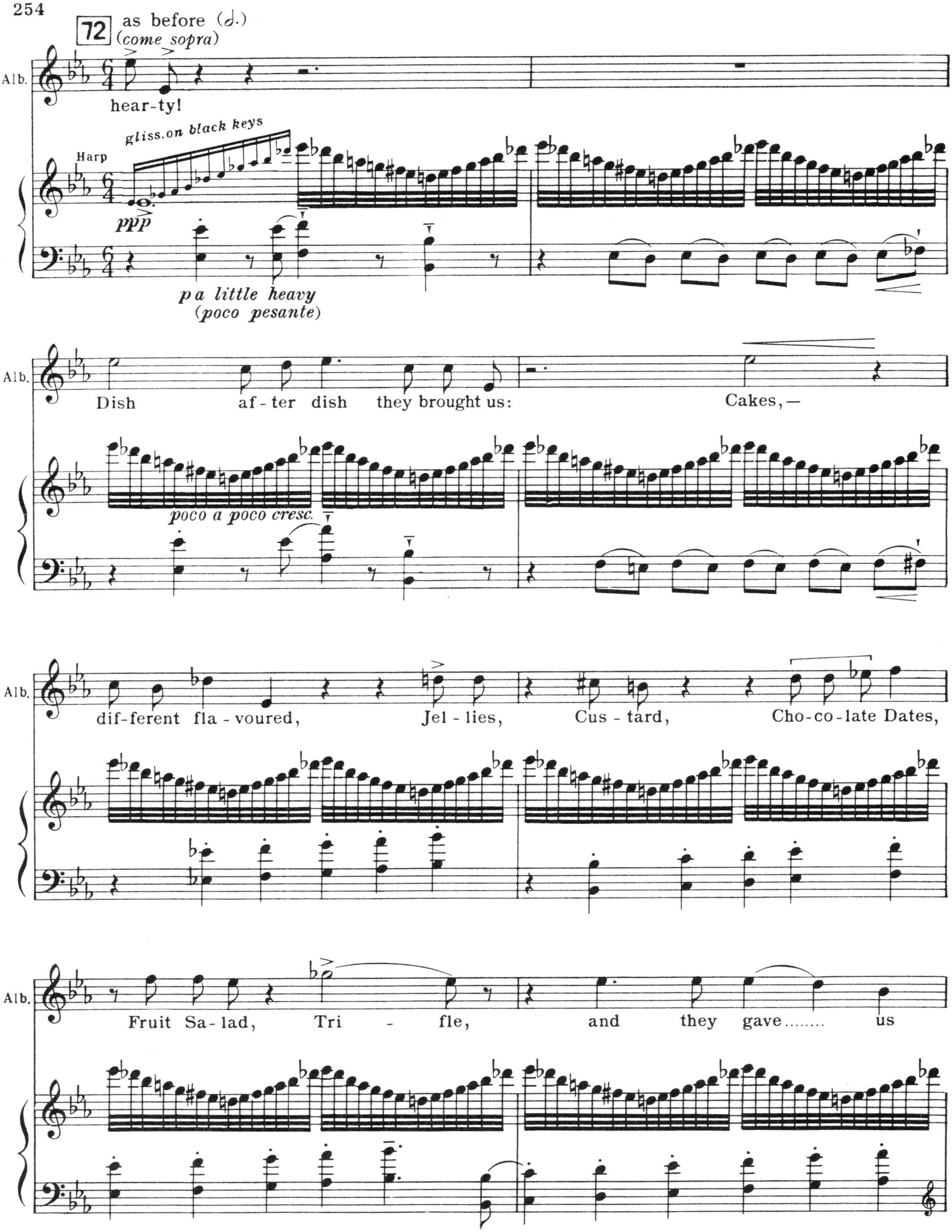
72
as before (𝅗𝅥.)
(come sopra)
Alb.
hear-ty!
Harp
gliss. on black keys
ppp
pa little heavy
(poco pesante)
Dish after dish they brought us: Cakes,—
poco a poco cresc.
dif-ferent fla-voured, Jel-lies, Cus-tard, Cho-co-late Dates,
Fruit Sa-lad, Tri - fle, and they gave........ us

Alb.
Pas-tries fresh - ly made With cream in,........ followed by Al - mond
sempre cresc.
Fa - vours! But Oh! .... The
ff
gliss.
73
W.W.
ffz
4
taste of that le-mon - ade!..... Won-der how it's made?
5
p
dim.
pp
freely
(ad lib.)
Nan-cy knows, I sup-pose. Nan-cy will know_ Pret-ty name, Nan-cy!
fp
sf pp
f

74
Slow, beginning quietly
(Lento, cominciando tranquillo)
sweetly expr. (dolce espr.)
Alb.
Pretty name! Why did she stare..... Each time I looked up at
mf
p
Str.
pp sust.
(Harp)
her?............. più Why was she watching.... When - e-ver I turned of a
più
sud-den?......... 75 p Nancy! cresc. Why did she blush.....
più
p cresc.
Catching my eye as she passed?..... f What made her stammer........ When
f
più f

stringendo
Alb.
speaking to me in that manner? Nan-cy?...... Nan-cy?...
f sempre più
ff
...... No, she be-longs to Sid, not me: We ne-ver
freely (ad lib.)
76
a little more movement (poco più mosso) 𝅗𝅥 = 76
with force (con forza)
ffz
(trem.)
ppp very short (staccatiss.)
talked or walked Light-heart-ed-ly through the woods, Nor shall that I can
see. Girls..... don't care for chaps like me: I'm too shy to re-
fpp
pp

Alb.
-ply .... En - ter - tain-ing - ly........when they speak, ...
cresc.
77
ff
I .... lose my nerve and fly, ...
f marked
poco a poco dim.
meno f
lose my nerve and fly! ....
molto rall.
Vla.
espr.
pp
Vc.
f
p
Sid is heard whistling down the street.
Sid's whistle (off)
78
Rather quick ♩ = 108
(Allegretto)
ppp freely (ad lib.)
pp freely (ad lib.)
D.B.
(espr.)
Str.
pizz.

ALBERT
pp
Sounds like Sid...... se-ren-ad-ing under her window,
light
pp (leggiero)
Im - pa-tient at
pp
dying away
(morendo)
Alb.
wait - ing, im - pa-tient-ly ach - - ing to take
pp
Nan-cy chas - ing love and ad-ven - ture!
cresc.
Sid's whistle (nearer)
tr
mf
f
79
slower (più lento)
rather heavy (poco pesante)
Sid does-n't suf-fer from shy-ness, ti-mid-i - ty,
W.W.
Str.

poco a poco cresc. ed accel.
Alb.
Gets what he wants by di - rect-ness, sim-pli-ci-ty, Aims at his tar-get with
cresc.
Alb.
shameless au - da-ci-ty, Trades on the fact of his ruth-less ten-a-ci-ty!
Sid and Nancy appear outside the shop window under the lamp-post. Albert drops back into shadow to watch them.
Recit.
Sid's whistle.
NANCY pp
You oughtn't to whis-tle! I told you that, Sid!
SID indignantly
It's pe-ri-shing cold standing here in the street! Twen-ty-five minutes!—
più f
Piano
più

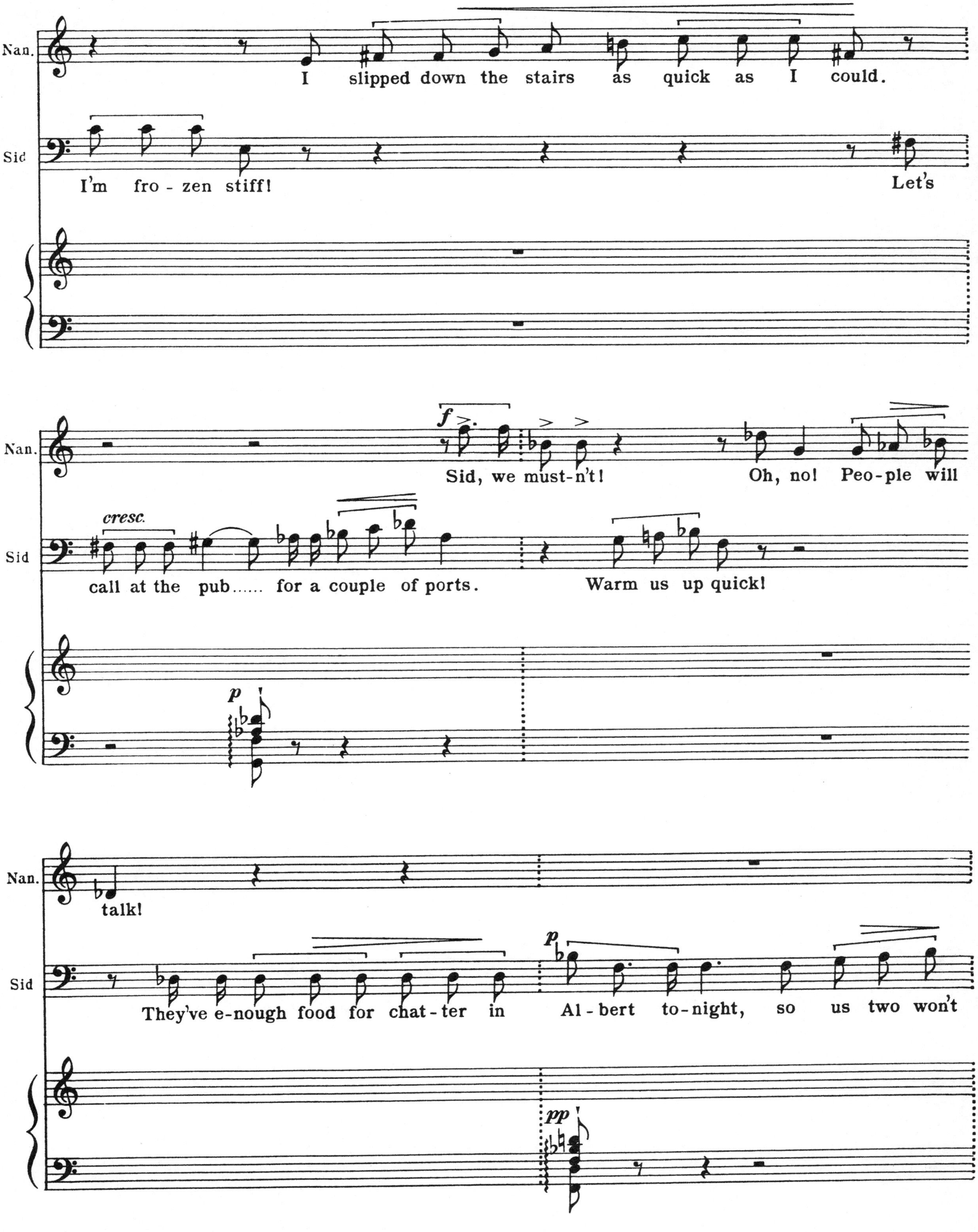
Nan.
Sid
I slipped down the stairs as quick as I could.
I'm fro - zen stiff! Let's
f
Sid, we must-n't! Oh, no! Peo-ple will
cresc.
call at the pub...... for a couple of ports. Warm us up quick!
p
talk!
They've e-nough food for chat - ter in Al - bert to-night, so us two won't
pp

sweetly and smooth
pp (dolce e legato)
sempre pp
Nan.
Poor kid! It does seem wrong to show him off to eve-ry-one.....
pp
Sid
matter.
pp
with Ped.
Nan.
.... like a sort of plas-ter saint or.... the vil-lage sim-ple-ton.....
pp
with more force
(con più forza)
Sid
O, he's all
cresc.
più
Nan.
But how can he sow them,
Sid
right, once he's sown a few wild oats, he'll live that down.

B. & H. 16241

Nan.
Sid
p
tied to his Mum?
lively (vivace)
f
I've done my share provid-ing the rum! Are
lively (vivace)
f
you vo-lun-tee-ring to cheer him...... a-long the a-gree - a-ble......
pp
rhythmic (ritmico)
f
pp
cresc.
NANCY
f
Of course not!
p
Still, I'd like to
prim-rose path?
f
pp
help!
solemn
Hea-ven helps those who help themselves!
pp
It's getting terri-ble chil-ly—
pp
pp

Nan.
It-'ll be ter-ri-ble cold up there on the Common.
Sid
pp
You need-n't be frigh-tened with
Slow
(Lento)
rall.
80
Sid comes close to Nancy.
Rather quick ♩= 108
(Allegretto)
pp
me!
Come a-long, dar-ling, come... fol-low me quick!
A.Fl.
Hrn.
B.Cl.
p
pp
Time is rac-ing us .... round..... the clock, Tick-ing and tock-ing our
evening a-way Which we hoped.. for .... and longed for all
(pp)
pp

81
pp
Nan.
Hur - ry to work, Hur - ry to play, Youth must hur - ry..........
Sid
pp
day! Hur-ry to work, Hur - ry to play, Hur -
81
Strgs. p
W.W.
Nan.
...... at...head-long pace, Seiz - ing and squeezing the plea-sures of life
Sid
- ry at...... head-long pace, Seiz-ing and squeezing the plea-sures of
p
Nan.
cresc.
in a cheer-ful, a cheer-ful .... and a fear - ful em -
Sid
cresc.
life, cheer - ful, cheer - ful, fear - ful...
cresc.

Nan.
Sid
f
-brace. Hur-ry to work,
dim.
Hur-ry to play,............
p
Youth
Nan - cy!........................... Nan - cy! ....
più p
Nan-cy! ....
mf
...... must hur - ry .... hur - ry!...
rall.
82
slower (più lento)
...... Nan - cy!................. Give us a kiss, Nan - cy!
pp
w.w.
Harp
ppp (Ped.)
mf
Not here in the light!
more marked (più marc.)
Windows have eyes!
Kiss me!
più f
Kiss me!
Str.
più f

A long passionate kiss.
83
quasi gliss.
accelerando
cresc.
animated
(animato)
NANCY
SID
ff
84
poco a
Time........ is a glut-ton,
Time........ is a glut-ton,
animated
(animato)
84
ff
poco a
poco dim.
Nan.
time.... is a thief, Youth must challenge him......... as......... he flies,...............
poco dim.
Sid.
time.... is a thief, Youth must challenge him......... as......... he flies,...............
relaxing
(rilassando)
relaxing -
(rilassando)
poco dim.
They go off down the street.
Nan.
Dar-ing and sharing its dreams of de - light........ ....
Sid.
Dar-ing and sharing its dreams of de - light........ ....
Harp
p

Albert emerges from the shadow in horror and embarrassment.
85
Nan.
mf
Be-tween eight........
p
and e - lev - en
Sid
mf
Be-tween eight..........
p
and e - lev - en
85
pp Str.
Harp
Str.
più p
pp
at...... night!......
at..... night!......
pp
at..... night!.......
at.... night!...............
ppp Str. harmonics
ALBERT
freely
(ad lib.)
pp
"Hea - ven helps those....... who help them-
night!..........................
night!...................................

86 Agitated (Agitato)
Alb.
Nan.
Sid
mf cresc.
ff
ppp
- selves."
"Help my-self!"........
O go,.......
Ah ....
Ah ....
Str.
ff
fff W.W.
...... Go!..... Go a-way! and leave me here a - lone .... With doubts and
Str.
ff
fff W.
87 ♩= 132
ter - rors you have ne - ver known!
ff Strgs.
sim.
sim.
p

bitterly
(amaramente)
Alb.
En - joy your evening as you will!
w.w.
sfpp sub.
heavy (pesante)
Kiss .... and hug your fill! em - brace ....
Hrn.
...... un - til the stars spin round .... like Cath-er-ine - wheels ....
cresc.
with force
(con forza)
.... A - gainst the rain - - - - - - - - -
mf

88
Alb.
- - - - - bow col-oured hills!
p
pp
(pp)
cresc.
Then hur-ry home at dawn, — Proud of what you've
done, — Smile, ... smile, ... smile, ...
cresc.
...... to think I .... slept a-lone!
mf

89
Alb.
ff
Nan - cy pi-ties me! Sid...... laughs!
f
Str.
w.w.
ffp
ff
Str.
ffp
ff
Very animated
(Animato molto)
simply
(semplice)
O - thers snigger at my sim - pli - ci - ty
sf
w.
pp
cresc.
mf
f
p
Of - fer me buns to stay in my cage
90
p cresc.
Pa -
pp
cresc.
mf
f
pp
molto
- rade me a - round as their white - head-ed boy!
cresc.
mf
cresc.
f sempre più

Always animated
(Sempre animato)
91
Alb.
ff
"Al-bert the Good!" Al - bert who
Str.pizz.
ff
w.w. p sust.
p
Should! Who Has - n't.... and Wouldn't if he Could! Al-bert the
più f
ff
p
p cresc.
92
Meek! Al - bert the Sheep! Missus Herring's guinea-pig! Missus Herring's
sf
ff
f
til-ly-pig! Mis-sus Herring's prig! But when, but when,
meno f
sff pp
w.w.
pp express.

Alb.
Shall I dare and dare a gain? How shall I screw my courage up To do
what must be done... by every-one?
cresc.
w.w.
ffz mf
93
always animating
(sempre animato) p
The tide will turn, the sun will set, while
sfp
Glock.
p
Harp
94
I stand here and hes - i - tate.....
p
The
l.h.
Fl.& Hrn.
p

Alb.
clock be-gins its rus-ty whirr, Cat-ches its breath ....
.... to strike the hour, ...
p
dim.
And of - fers me a
Vc. Cym.
p Clt.
fi - nal choice that must be ans - wered No .... or
ff
95
He hears the clink of coins in his pocket and takes out his purse of sovereigns.
Yes.
p
Forgotten those!
My virgin ransom!
pp
Harp Solo
Str. pizz. sf
f
Str. (pizz.)

He picks out one sovereign.
Alb.
f
freely
(ad lib.)
I'll toss for it, and damn the risk!
Rather quick
(Allegretto)
96
rhythmic
p (ritmico)
Een - ey, meen-ey,
Ob.
Bsn.
ppp without expr.
(senza espr.)
Str.
f
Str.
Ob.
p
min - ey mo, Heads for Yes and tails for No, Tails for No and heads for Yes.......
He tosses the coin, and puts his foot on it, where it falls.
rall.
.... Spin it up!
Ob.
tr
p
f
Harp
gliss. on black keys
ppp
D.B.
lunga
Heads!!!
Slow (Lento)
Looking at it grimly.
p solemn
Well, you've gone and done it now!.....
Hrn.
Bsn.
pp
Str.
lunga

poco a poco cresc.
Alb.
It's very plain, you've burnt your boats... and can't go back a-gain.
poco a poco cresc.
Sid's whistle is heard in the distance.
Alb.
O gol-ly! But how... but how...
SID'S whistle (off)
ff
pp
(pizz.)
ALBERT whistling in imitation.
p hesitant
(esitando)
pp Str.
With sudden resolve Albert stuffs the purse into his pocket, seizes his hat and an old mackintosh, and slips out through the door into the street. We see him go past the window and down the street.
97
Rather quick as before
(Allegretto come sopra)
ppp Str.

*) At the original production of the Opera this Cadenza was whistled:

Mum
(p)
Al-bert!
p
Fast a - sleep, poor kid! Worn
ppp
out by all this fuss:
sweetly
pp (dolce)
Sleep - ing the sleep of the
just! .... And rich-er by twent - y-five
sempre pp
pp
quid.
She yawns.
Ooo .... aah! Ooo aah!
Ob.
ppp sweetly (dolce)

Mum locks up the shop, pulls down the blinds and trudges wearily up to bed.
100
a little more movement (slower than at the start)
(poco più mosso (più lento che prima))
I shan't need rock-ing my-self!
Str. pizz.
pp
rall. molto
Slow as before but a little hesitant
(Lento come sopra ma poco esitando)
A. Fl.
ppp sweetly (dolce)
B. Cl. ppp
sweetly (dolce)
B. Fl.
ppp
SLOW CURTAIN
pizz.
pppp
End of Act II

ACT III

Very fast 𝅗𝅥. = 112
(Prestissimo)
ppp
Side Drum
Vc.
D.B.
Bsn.
1
short
(stacc.)
poco
pp
Cl
2

3
cresc.
più f cresc.
f
l.h.
4
ff Str.
w.w.
sonorous
5
w.w.
pp subito
6
f
ff

7
Hn.
ff marcatissimo
dim.
8
Fl.
pp marked
p
pp
cresc.
9
f
pp
Ob.
dim.
Cl.
mf
Bsn.
p

10
pp marked
Harp
Str.
pp express.
11
pp sempre
Cl.
Bsn.
Fl.
Ob.
pp
12
13
sempre pp

14
dim.
ppp
CURTAIN
Mrs. Herring's greengrocery shop. The afternoon of May the Second.
Nancy is alone in the shop, miserably polishing the scales.
15
Bsn.
ppp
Cl.
p very sweetly (dolciss.)
p
Str. pizz.
freely (ad lib.)
16
a tempo
p
freely (ad lib.)
a tempo
mf
freely (ad lib.)
17
a tempo
più f
pp

Bsn.
Cl.
7
pp
cresc.
mf
D.B.
S.D.
freely
(ad lib.)
18
a tempo
p
più f
cresc.
f
a tempo
19
pp
Bsn.
Ob.
Fl.
cresc.

Emmie dashes past the window and into the shop. Nancy silences her.

Em.
Nan.
se.
Fe - lo de what?
p
cresc.
f
Done him-self in!
f
pp
Un-less he's been murdered!
CIS appearing at the window.
21 as before (come sopra)
f
Come on, Em-mie!
Nan.
f
Oh no!..... no!......
21 as before (come sopra)
Str.
ff tr
pp
(con Ped.)
S.D.
EMMIE
with spirit
f (con spirito)
I'm run - ning off now to join in the
Cis
Got your compass?
Picc. pp

Em.
hunt Round Has - ke - ton Hall with the Pee - wit Pa -
cresc.
freely (ad lib.)
ff
- trol! .... Ta - ta!
ff
Bsn.
f
22 Rather slow (𝅗𝅥) (Andante)
Emmie and Cis run off.
NANCY poco f
What would Mis-sus Her-ring say?...
Cl.
7
f
fp
Str. Harp mf expr.
freely (ad lib.)
3
Nan.
What would every-bo-dy think?...
If they knew the trick we played
freely (ad lib.)
fp
fp
freely (ad lib.)

Nan.
Giv-ing Albert rum to drink
pp
We did it for
dim.
pp expr.
Recit.
fun! Oh, we should - n't have done! shouting (off)
MAYOR
ff
[Police whistle off.] Hi! Don't for-get the splints!
dim.
S.D.
23
(pizz.)
Cl.
7
ff
f
Bsn.
più f
Now he's vanished o - ver-night,...
freely (ad lib.)
fp
mf
Dis-appeared without a trace....
And I bit-ter-ly re - gret...
freely (ad lib.)
freely (ad lib.)
fp

Nan.
What I did in thought-lessness
pp
We did it for
fp
pp expr.
Recit.
fun: O, we should-n't have done!
HARRY shouting through the window
They're dragging the Millpond with ropes and ruddy great hooks!
dim.
S.Dr.
ppp
24
more agitated
(più agitato)
f
Bring him back, O bring him back!...
freely
(ad lib.)
ff
Cl
Bsn.
ff
f expr.
Safe and sound in life and limb.
dim.
Missus Herring's heart will break...
fp
meno f
fp
dim.

Nan.
Losing him, losing him!
pp
We did it for fun, Oh we
cresc.
ppexpr.
cresc.
Recit.
should-n't, we should - n't have done!
SID appears at the door, shouting back at someone
f
What the hell d'you think I am?— a human bloodhound?
ppp
poco f
S. D.
ppp
Sid!
thank good-ness you've come!
Sid
mf cresc.
I've spent the whole blooming day,
Piano
f
mf
Splashing a - round, up to my neck in wa-ter and clay, And for all that I
cresc.

NANCY
Not...?
p
Thank hea-vens!
Sid
found —
p
— One maggot-ty sheep lying dead on the ground!
pp
ff
MAYOR (off)
ff
NO!..
25
Quick and heavy ♩(♩.) = 112
(Allegro pesante)
Sid
f
I'm hun-gry, I'm
SUPERINTENDENT (shouting off)
ff heavy (pesante)
A - ny more news..... a-bout Al-bert?
Quick and heavy ♩(♩.) = 112
(Allegro pesante)
25
Tutti
(6/8)
pp
molto cresc.
ff
Sid
tired, I'm sick of the sound of "Al-bert! Al - bert! Al-bert! Al-bert!" all

NANCY
f furious (furioso)
You're heart-less and sel-fish and thoughtless and
Sid
round.
Ob.
f very marked
Bsn.
Str. f
Nan.
cruel! No con-science or feel-ings of kind-ness at all!
Sid
f
He is-n't the
mf
mf
f
mf
Nan.
f
You've
Sid
first and he won't be the last, To throw up his heels and kick o-ver the

26
meno f
Nan.
ru-ined poor Al-bert, you've ru-ined his Mum, and I hope you're con -
Sid
mark.
He is - n't the first and he won't be the
p
f
mf
- tent - ed...
I hope you're con - tent - ed...
last,
To throw up his heels and kick o - ver the mark.
But why car-ry
mf cresc.
You've ru - ined poor Al - bert, you've
cresc.
on as if Al-bert had gone, as if Al-bert had gone, as if Al - bert had

Nan.
Sid
ru - ined his Mum,..... and I hope you're con - tent - ed with
gone on a one-way ex - cur-sion to King-dom Come, to King-dom Come, to King-dom
27
what .... you've done! Ex -
Come?..............................
You're talking as though I'd done all I
dim.
-cus - es are use - less__ So don't try them
could__ To wipe out the fam-'ly of Her-rings for good.
cresc.

Nan.
Sid
on! I'm sor - ry we did it, I'm
But all I in - tend - ed and all that I planned, was giv - ing young
cresc.
sor - ry I helped you, in fu - ture I'll
Al - bert a bro - ther - ly hand, was giv - ing Al - bert, Al - bert, Al - bert, Al -
f
cresc.
Recit.
The Superintendent interrupts their quarrel.
ff
leave you to your - self! ....
- bert, Al - bert, Al - bert a hand! ....
SUPERINTENDENT
Mis - sus Her - ring a - bout?
S.D.

Nan.
She's rest-ing.
Sup.
Ask her down! Of-fi-cial business. Won't keep her long.
Nancy goes off to fetch Mrs. Herring.
28
Very fast ♩. = 112
(Prestissimo (Tempo primo))
W.W.
pp cresc.
ff
G. P.
ff
G. P.
ff pp
Hn.
29
Slow, as if recitative
(Lento quasi recitativo)
SID p
How's the man-hunt?
SUPERINTENDENT f heavy (pesante)
Give me.........
heavy (pesante)
Str.
ff
sf
pp
[B.D.]
Sup.
..... a decent murder with a corpse! —
[Tria.]
ff
sf
sf
9
9

Sup.
f
Give.... me a clear-cut case of ar - son!
ffz
ff
Give me a robber-y with force! –
freely
(ad lib.)
Or a crim-i-nal case of
5
express.
sf
[Whip]
[Gong]
30
Very fast (Prestissimo (Tempo primo))
rape!
sempre f
but
(ma più
But
pp
S.D.
sempre sim.
Bsn.
smoother
legato)
God pre - serve me.................. from these dis - ap - pear - ing

Sup.
cas - es, Where eve - ry - one from the
Cl.
ba - ker to the Non-con-formist par - son Turns
Sher - lock Holmes and pokes a - round find - ing
ev - i - dence in the most un - like - ly
pla - ces.
sim. molto cresc.

Recit.
HARRY (yelling through the door)
ff
Su - per! La-dy Billows wants you up at her house! Im-med-i - ate!
sf
fp
31 Very fast (Prestissimo) (𝅗𝅥.)
SUPERINTENDENT (𝅗𝅥. = 𝅘𝅥)
Broadly
(Largamente)
ff
My La-dy Bil-lows!..... Self-
w.w.
mf cresc.
ff
Str.
f
Hrn.
Sup.
- - ap-pointed Chief........ Con-sta-ble!
ff
dim.
pp
Harp
Nancy comes back supporting Mum, who is dressed in deep black.
32 Less movement 𝅘𝅥 = 63
(Meno mosso)
MUM
pp
Have you
pp Ob.
sorrowful (dolente)
Fl.

Mum
found him?
He's dead... and gone... poor
SUPERINTENDENT
pp
Not yet
pp
Al-bert's dead and gone...
It's the living truth. Dead and
33
NANCY p(dolce) sweetly
Don't say that!
33
gone! dead and gone! In the pride of his youth, the pride of his youth...
più p
SUPERINTENDENT
pp tenderly (teneramente)
I've come to ask for a pho-to-graph, To send round the sta-tions for i-den-ti-fi-

Mum
Sup.
pp
There's one in a frame on the whats-is-name, A-bove the Bib-le, on the tu-lip-wood
-ca-tion.
Nancy goes to fetch it.
34
sweetly
p(dolce)
ta-ble.
It was took on the pier at Fe-lixstowe, when his
mf Harp
more marked
Dad was a-live, in a stu-di-o...
We paid three and six to have it en-
marked
Nancy brings in the photo and Mum clasps it to herself.
-larged and a-no-ther three bob for the frame and the glass.
poco dim.

passionate
ff (appass.)
35
Mum
It is all that I have to re-
Tutti
espress.
- member him by, — all, all, all that remains of my dar - ling boy!
all! all! all!
All that re-
Ob.
Fl.
Harp
- mains... of the ba - by I bore with such pains, all,....
dim.
36
The Mayor appears at the window and excitedly beckons the Superintendent and Sid, who tip-toe out. Mum doesn't notice.
all that re - mains, all,... all,... all,... all,... all,....
pp
S.D.
sim.
pp sempre

At the same speed (L'istesso tempo)
always rather marked (like a lament)
37
pp (sempre poco marcato (come un lamento))
Mum
All, all...... that I did,.... all...... that I did....
Vlns., Harp
pp smooth (legato)
Cl.
Vc.
Mum
All..... that I planned was build - ing in sand for Al - bert my
NANCY
pp sweetly (dolce)
He'll come back a - gain, my dear.
Mum
pp
boy is dead. Where did he go?.... where did he go?.....
pp
Miss Wordsworth and the Vicar come quietly in.
Nan.
He'll come back to you, I swear. Trust in that and
Mum
Why.... was he took; where - e - ver I look the world's full of

MISS WORDSWORTH
very smooth pp (legatiss.)
38
A grie - vous tor - ment for a
Nan.
(pp)
ne - ver fear...... He'll come back be - fore to-night,
Mum
(pp)
bit - ter woe. Life's be - come bleak, Life's be - come bleak,
VICAR
pp very smooth (legatiss.)
A grie - vous tor - ment for a
38
Fl.
sim.
D.B.
pp sweetly and sustained (dolce sost.)
Miss W.
moth - er's heart,........ a bit - ter
Nan.
He'll re-pent his sud - den flight, he'll re - turn, you'll
Mum
Life's be - come bare with - out.... Al-bert here to ease and re -
Vic
moth - er's heart,........ a bit - ter

Miss W.
blow .... to .... bear .... a - lone ... We
Nan.
see .... I'm right, He'll re-turn, you'll see .... I'm right ....
più
Mum
- lieve my grief, ease and re - lieve my grief.
più
Vic.
blow .... to .... bear .... a - lone ... We
più
39
Miss W.
(pp)
come to com - fort you and ease the
poco cresc.
Nan.
pp
He'll come back a - gain, my dear. He'll come back to
poco cresc.
Mum
pp
Where did he go, ... where did he go, ... why .... was he took; where -
poco cresc.
Vic.
(pp)
come to com - fort you and ease the
poco cresc.
39
pp
sim.
poco cresc.

Miss W.
Nan.
Mum
Vic.
smart..... with crumbs of Chris - tian con - so -
you, I swear. Trust in that and ne - ver fear, Trust in that and
ev - er I look the world's full of bit - ter woe, bit - ter
smart..... with crumbs of Chris - tian con - so -
dim.
40
- la - tion, to com - fort you and ease the
ne - ver fear, he'll come back, my dear, He'll come back to
woe All...................... that I did,.... all..... that I did,.....
- la - tion, to com - fort you and ease the
pp

Miss W.
smart,........ with crumbs of Chris - tian
Nan.
you, I swear. He'll.... come back be - fore to-night,
Mum
all..... that I planned was build - ing in sand for Al - bert is dead,
Vic.
smart,........ with crumbs of Chris - tian
Miss W.
con - so - la - tion, crumbs........ of
Nan.
Trust in that and ne - - ver fear, my dear, you'll
Mum
All..... that I planned was build - ing in sand for Al - bert is dead,
Vic.
con - so - la - tion, crumbs........ of

(Recit.)
Miss W.
con - so - la - - - - tion.....
HARRY shouting through the window
Hi! Hi! Heard the news? Heard the news?
Nan.
see I'm right. You'll see I'm right, you'll see!....
Mum
Al - bert is dead, Al - bert, my son, is dead.
Vic.
con - so - la - - - - tion.....
S.D.
Har.
There's a Big White Some-thing in Missus Wil-liams' well!
41 a tempo
Mum
O God! it's him!
41
Mum collapses in Nancy's arms.
NANCY
No, no, I'm sure it is-n't him, I'm sure it is-n't him, No, I'm
dim.
poco a poco dim.
Cl.
f espr.

MISS WORDSWORTH pp
In such an hour we scarcely
Nan.
sure it is-n't him, I'm sure it is-n't him.
No!
VICAR pp
In such an hour we scarcely
pp
Miss W.
dare pre-tend we have the power to help our friend!
ppp
LADY BILLOWS (off) p
Fools....
Nan.
No! No, I'm sure it is-n't him!
Vic.
dare pre-tend we have the power to help our friend!
ppp
42 Very animated
(Molto animato)
(nearer) mf
Ldy. B.
..............................!!
Fools..........................
mf
f
più f

She comes in with Florence following her.
She appears at the door.
Ldy. B.
.....!! Blund-er-ing fools.........! Budd's the
with force
(con forza)
worst! I'll ring up Scot-land Yard my-self! We must have
43
ex - perts down to help! A de-tec - tive in-spec-tor:
marked
Won't.... ac-cept less, won't ac-cept less! Dis -
Bsn.

Ldy. B.
-patch'd by the Liverpool Street Ex-press ....
f
Yo - kels!
NANCY p
The Saxmundham po - lice are out...
w.
very smooth (legatiss.)
pp
f
sweetly
MISS WORDSWORTH (dolce)
If on-ly they could find him!
Ldy. B.
Bump-kins!
VICAR p
And the Wickham Market Mi - li-tia...
pp
f
pp
44
cresc.
Ldy. B.
Find him! Find him! Find him!
ff
freely (ad lib.)
I'd soon find the wretched boy!......
FLORENCE p
The
44
cresc.
ff
ff

45 As at the start (Tempo primo)
sempre f
Ldy. B.
Mod-ern me-thods!...
rhythmic and clear
(ritmico e distinto)
Flo.
whole of the dis-trict from Lox-ford to Ips-wich is seek-ing and
45 As at the start (Tempo primo)
pp Harp
Str.
ppp
That's..... what we need!
Blood-hounds!...
searching-ing in vain—
And run-ning a-round without rea-son or
Fin-ger-prints!...
E-lec-tro-mag-nets!
cresc.
rhyme—
Wast-ing their en-er-gy, mon-ey and time........................

46
Ldy. B.
f
Wa - - - ter di - vi-ners!
Flo.
mf
Pok - ing their no-ses in - to each o-ther's hou - ses. Snatch - ing at
46
pp
Hn.
marked
Fl.
47
Call in Co-nan Doyle...... Te - le - graph..... the STRAND MA-GA-
clues...... that sim - ply con-fuse........ and start - ing new ru-mours to keep up the
47
- ZINE..... He'll bring him back, dead or a - live! dead....
cresc.
game, start-ing new ru - mours to keep up the game,.... to keep up the
più f
cresc.

Ldy. B.
Flo.
48
f
marked
ff
più f
or a - live!
game!
A cri - sis like this can't be
left to the lo - cals
We must call on ex - pert ad -
- vice, we must call on ex - pert ad - vice!

A small and solemn procession comes down the street _ Sid, the Superintendent and the Mayor _
very animated (molto animato)
49
fff
S.D.
sim.
sfp
bringing a tray covered with a white cloth. _ They enter the shop. _ Mum fearfully approaches the tray,
lifts the cloth and sees Albert's small orange-blossom crown lying there _ crushed and muddied.
poco a poco rall. ma senza dim.
50
(senza dim.)
sempre più rall.
(ffz)
Slow (Lento)
MUM (screaming)
She faints.
lunga
My Al-bert's wreath!
MAYOR p solemn
. . . Found on the road to Campsey Ash...
SUPERINTENDENT p solemn
...Crushed by a cart...
Bells
Tutti
pp

Threnody

All gather pitifully around the wreath. Nancy shuts the door and pulls down the shop-blinds.

Miss W.
Si-lent, swift and mer - - - ci-ful. In the midst of life is death,
Ldy. B.
Si-lent, swift and mer - - - ci-ful. In the midst of life is death;
Nan.
Si-lent, swift and mer - - - ci-ful. In the midst of life is death,
Mum
Si-lent, swift and mer - - - ci - ful. In the midst of life is death,
Flo.
Si-lent, swift and mer - - - ci - ful. In the midst of life is death,
May.
Si-lent, swift and mer - - - ci - ful. In the midst of life is death,
Sid
Si-lent, swift and mer - - - ci - ful. In the midst of life is death,
Solo
pp express.
Vic.
Si-lent, swift and mer - - - ci-ful. Sigh
Sup.
Si-lent, swift and mer - - - ci-ful. In the midst of life is death,
ppp

Miss W.
Death a-waits us one and all: Death attends our smallest step, Silent, swift and mer -
Ldy.B.
Death a-waits us one and all: Death attends our smallest step, Silent, swift and mer -
Nan.
Death a-waits us one and all: Death attends our smallest step, Silent, swift and mer -
Mum
Death a-waits us one and all: Death attends our smallest step, Silent, swift and mer -
Flo.
Death a-waits us one and all: Death attends our smallest step, Silent, swift and mer -
May.
Death a-waits us one and all: Death attends our smallest step, Silent, swift and mer -
Sid
Death a-waits us one and all: Death attends our smallest step, Silent, swift and mer -
Vic.
sigh for youth..... that scorns to die, and leaps in-to e-ter-ni-ty with
Sup.
Death a-waits us one and all: Death attends our smallest step, Silent, swift and mer -

52
Miss W.
- ci-ful. In the midst of life is death, Death a-waits us one and all:
Ldy. B.
- ci-ful. In the midst of life is death, Death a-waits us one and all:
Nan.
Solo
pp
weeping (piangendo)
.... Why............was he born who had to run so short a race and die.....
Mum
- ci - ful. In the midst of life is death, Death a-waits us one and all:
Flo.
- ci - ful. In the midst of life is death, Death a-waits us one and all:
May.
- ci - ful. In the midst of life is death, Death a-waits us one and all:
Sid
- ci - ful. In the midst of life is death, Death a-waits us one and all:
Vic.
ppp
in-nocent simpli-ci - ty...the midst of life is death, Death a-waits us one and all:
Sup.
- ci-ful. In the midst of life is death, Death a-waits us one and all:
52
ppp

Miss W.
Death at-tends our smallest step, Si-lent, swift and mer - - - ci - ful.
Ldy. B.
Death at-tends our smallest step, Si-lent, swift and mer - - - ci - ful.
Nan.
express.
ppp
die... so young!.... fore-doomed to fall be-fore be-gun? ...mer - ci - ful.
Mum
Death at-tends our smallest step, Si-lent, swift and mer - - ci - ful.
Flo.
Death at-tends our smallest step, Si-lent, swift and mer - - ci - ful.
May.
Solo
marked and heroic
(marcato ed eroico)
Death at-tends our smallest step, Si-lent, swift... He.... died, he died too soon,
Sid
Death at-tends our smallest step, Si-lent, swift and mer - - ci - ful.
Vic.
Death at-tends our smallest step, Si-lent, swift and mer - - - ci - ful.
Sup.
Death at-tends our smallest step, Si-lent, swift and mer - - - ci - ful.
ppp

Miss W.
In the midst of life is death, Death a-waits us one and all:
Ldy.B.
In the midst of life is death, Death a-waits us one and all:
Nan.
In the midst of life is death, Death a-waits us one and all:
Mum
In the midst of life is death, Death a-waits us one and all:
Flo.
In the midst of life is death, Death a-waits us one and all:
May.
sempre marcatiss.
.... death .... came, death came be - fore his bud had blossomed in - to
Sid
In the midst of life is death, Death a-waits us one and all:
Vic.
In the midst of life is death, Death a-waits us one and all:
Sup.
In the midst of life is death, Death a-waits us one and all:

Miss W.
Death at-tends our smal-lest step, Si-lent, swift and mer - -
Ldy. B.
Death at-tends our smal-lest step, Si-lent, swift and mer
Nan.
Death at-tends our smal-lest step, Si-lent, swift and mer - -
Mum
Death at-tends our smal-lest step, Si-lent, swift and mer - -
Flo.
Death at-tends our smal-lest step, Si-lent, swift and mer - -
May.
ff
flower, and we shall see his like no more— and we shall see his
Sid
Death at-tends our smal-lest step, Si-lent, swift and mer - -
Vic.
Death at-tends our smal-lest step, Si-lent, swift and mer - -
Sup.
Death at-tends our smal-lest step, Si-lent, swift and mer - -

53
Miss W.
più f
- - ci - ful _ In the midst of life is death, Death a-waits us one and all:
Ldy. B.
Solo brilliant
.... Weep for him .... O weep for him, whose sim - ple fame shone clearly
Nan.
più f
- - ci - ful _ In the midst of life is death, Death a-waits us one and all:
Mum
più f
- ci - ful _ In the midst of life is death, Death a-waits us one and all:
Flo.
più f
- ci - ful _ In the midst of life is death, Death a-waits us one and all:
May.
più f
like... no........ more. In the midst of life is death, Death a-waits us one and all:
Sid
più f
- ci - ful _ In the midst of life is death, Death a-waits us one and all:
Vic.
più f
- - ci - ful _ In the midst of life is death, Death a-waits us one and all:
Sup.
più f
- - ci - ful _ In the midst of life is death, Death a-waits us one and all:
53
ppp
poco più f

Miss W.
Death attends our smallest step, Si-lent, swift and mer - - - ci-ful
Ldy. B.
like a.... can-dle flame, blown bright... by.... the wind, then out a - gain!
Nan.
Death attends our smallest step, Si-lent, swift and mer - - - ci-ful
Mum
Death attends our smallest step, Si-lent, swift and mer - - ci - ful
Flo.
Death attends our smallest step, Si-lent, swift and mer - - ci - ful
May.
Death attends our smallest step, Si-lent, swift and mer - - ci - ful
Sid
Death attends our smallest step, Si-lent, swift and mer - - ci - ful
Vic.
Death attends our smallest step, Si-lent, swift and mer - - ci - ful
Sup.
Solo f heavy (pesante)
Death attends our smallest step, Si-lent, swift and mer.............................. Heavy

Miss W.
cresc.
In the midst of life is death, Death a-waits us one and all,
Ldy.B.
cresc.
In the midst of life is death, Death a-waits us one and all,
Nan.
cresc.
In the midst of life is death, Death a-waits us one and all,
Mum
cresc.
In the midst of life is death, Death a-waits us one and all,
Flo.
cresc.
In the midst of life is death, Death a-waits us one and all,
May.
cresc.
In the midst of life is death, Death a-waits us one and all,
Sid
cresc.
In the midst of life is death, Death a-waits us one and all,
Vic.
cresc.
In the midst of life is death, Death a-waits us one and all,
Sup.
cresc.
heart-ed we ask Why he was cho-sen for to die? But Death's not
cresc.

Miss W.
Death attends our smallest step, Si-lent, swift and mer - - - ci-ful _
Ldy. B.
Death attends our smallest step, Si-lent, swift and mer - - - ci-ful _
Nan.
Death attends our smallest step, Si-lent, swift and mer - - - ci-ful _
Mum
Death attends our smallest step, Si-lent, swift and mer - - - ci - ful _
Flo.
Solo f with force (con forza)
Death attends _ These flower's were a joyful sight and shone with pu-ri-ty and light...
ff
May.
Death attends our smallest step, Si-lent, swift and mer - - - ci - ful _
Sid
Death attends our smallest step, Si-lent, swift and mer - - - ci - ful _
Vic.
Death attends our smallest step, Si-lent, swift and mer - - - ci-ful _
Sup.
given to re - ply! ... Si-lent, swift and mer - - - ci-ful _
f

54
dim. poco a poco
lamenting (lamentoso)
Solo
Miss W.
Yes - ter - day these flowers were fresh .... With gai - e -
Ldy. B.
f dim.
In the midst of life is death, Death a - waits us one and all:
Nan.
In the midst of life is death, Death a - waits us one and all:
Mum
In the midst of life is death, Death a - waits us one and all:
Flo.
...... Till Death struck at them o - ver - night! ... one and all:
May.
In the midst of life is death, Death a - waits us one and all:
Sid
In the midst of life is death, Death a - waits us one and all:
Vic.
In the midst of life is death, Death a - waits us one and all:
Sup.
In the midst of life is death, Death a - waits us one and all:
54
dim.

Miss W.
Ldy. B.
Nan.
Mum
Flo.
May.
Sid
Vic.
Sup.
dim.
-ty and love-li-ness_ To-day they fade to ug-li-ness, to ug - li -
Death attends our smallest step, Si-lent, swift and mer - - - ci-ful_
Death attends our smallest step, Si-lent, swift and mer - - - ci-ful_
Death attends our smallest step, Si-lent, swift and mer - - ci - ful_
Death attends our smallest step, Si-lent, swift and mer - - ci - ful_
Death attends our smallest step, Si-lent, swift and mer - - ci - ful_
Solo pp
Death attends our smallest step, Si-lent, swift and mer .... The
Death attends our smallest step, Si-lent, swift and mer - - ci - ful_
Death attends our smallest step, Si-lent, swift and mer - - ci - ful_
ppp

55
Miss W.
ppp
-ness, the midst of life is death, Death a-waits us one and all:
Ldy.B.
ppp
In the midst of life is death, Death a-waits us one and all:
Nan.
ppp
In the midst of life is death, Death a-waits us one and all:
Mum
ppp
In the midst of life is death, Death a-waits us one and all:
Flo.
ppp
In the midst of life is death, Death a-waits us one and all:
May.
ppp
In the midst of life is death, Death a-waits us one and all:
Sid
solemn
grave's a fine.............. and pri-vate place, but hor - ri-bly cold and
Vic.
ppp
In the midst of life is death, Death a-waits us one and all:
Sup.
ppp
In the midst of life is death, Death a-waits us one and all:
55

56
Miss W.
cresc.
Death attends our smallest step, Si - lent, swift,— In the midst of life is death,
Ldy. B.
cresc.
Death attends our smallest step, Si - lent, swift,— In the midst of life is death,
Nan.
cresc.
Death attends our smallest step, Si - lent, swift,— In the midst of life is death,
Mum
Solo f passionate (appassionato)
Death attends our smallest step, Si - lent, swift,— Al - bert! Al-bert!
Flo.
cresc.
Death attends our smallest step, Si - lent, swift,— In the midst of life is death,
May.
cresc.
Death attends our smallest step, Si - lent, swift,— In the midst of life is death,
Sid
cresc.
hor-ri-bly chaste, And not at - trac-tive to my taste. The midst of life is death,
Vic.
cresc.
Death attends our smallest step, Si - lent, swift,— In the midst of life is death,
Sup.
cresc.
Death attends our smallest step, Si - lent, swift,— In the midst of life is death,
56
cresc.

Miss W.
Death a - waits us one and all, he beck-ons us with ev - ery breath we
Ldy.B.
Death a - waits us one and all, he beck-ons us with ev - ery breath we
Nan.
Death a - waits us one and all, he beck-ons us with ev - ery breath we
Mum
cresc.
My on - ly son! Al - bert! My on - ly son! Flesh of my
Flo.
Death a - waits us one and all, he beck-ons us with ev - ery breath we
May.
Death a - waits us one and all, he beck-ons us with ev - ery breath we
Sid
Death a - waits us one and all, he beck-ons us with ev - ery breath we
Vic.
Death a - waits us one and all, he beck-ons us with ev - ery breath we
Sup.
Death a - waits us one and all, he beck-ons us with ev - ery breath we

Miss W.
take and does not he - si - tate To strike the hum - ble...... or the
Ldy. B.
take and does not he - si - tate To strike the hum - ble...... or the
Nan.
take and does not he - si - tate To strike the hum - ble...... or the
Mum
ff
flesh and bone of my bone — Let me die too........ now you are
Flo.
take and does not he - si - tate To strike the hum - ble...... or the
May.
take and does not he - si - tate To strike the hum - ble...... or the
Sid
take and does not he - si - tate To strike the hum - ble...... or the
Vic.
take and does not he - si - tate To strike the hum - ble...... or the
Sup.
take and does not he - si - tate To strike the hum - ble...... or the

57
animated (animato)
lamenting (lamentoso)
Miss W.
great............................ These flowers were fresh.... with gai - e - ty and
Ldy.B.
brilliant
great. Weep for... him..............
Nan.
weeping (piangendo)
great. Why.......... was he born who had.... to run so short a race..............
Mum
passionate (appassionato)
gone! Al - bert!...... Al - bert!..... My on-ly
Flo.
with force (con forza)
great. These flowers were a joy-ful sight and shone with pu-ri - ty and
May.
heroic (eroico)
great............................ He.................... died, he died too
Sid
solemn
great. The grave's a fine.................. and pri - vate place, but
Vic.
expressive
great. Sigh....................................... sigh.... for youth............. that scorns to
Sup.
great.
57
animated (animato)
p
Timp.

Miss W.
love-li - ness.... To-day they fade to ug-li-ness, to ug-li-
Ldy. B.
.... whose sim-ple fame shone clear-ly.... like a.... can-dle... flame ....
Nan.
.... and die,........ die.... so young .... fore-doomed to fall.... be-fore be-
Mum
son! Al - bert!..... Al - bert! My on-ly son!.............
Flo.
light .... Till death struck at them o - ver-night. These flow-ers
May.
soon .... death............ came, death came be-fore his bud had
Sid
hor - ri-bly cold and hor-ri-bly chaste, and not at-trac-tive
Vic.
die And leaps.... in - to e - ter - ni-ty with
heavy
(pesante)
ff
Sup.
Hea-vy - heart-ed we ask Why he was cho-sen for to
(p)

Miss W.
- ness. To - day.... they fade to ug - li - ness ....
Ldy. B.
...... Blown bright .... by.... the... wind, then out a-gain.
Nan.
- gun, fore - doomed to fall.... be - fore be - gun.
Mum
.... Al - bert!..... let..... me die now you are gone!
Flo.
were a joy - ful sight and shone with pu - ri - ty.
May.
bloomed and we shall see his like... no more.
Sid
to my taste, not at - trac - tive to my taste.
Vic.
in - no - cent sim - pli - ci - ty, in - no - cent sim - pli - ci - ty.
Sup.
die but death's not gi - ven to re - ply.
cresc.

58 Majestic
(Maestoso)
Miss W.
Ldy. B.
Nan.
Mum
Flo.
May.
Sid
Vic.
Sup.
ff broadly (largamente)
fz
Grief is si - lent,....... Pi - ty dumb; Des -
W.W.
Strgs.
ffz
heavy
ff (pesante)
Timp
D.B.

Miss W.
- pair exclaims in endless pain...... That one so fine should live.... in vain and die......
Ldy. B.
- pair exclaims in endless pain...... That one so fine should live.... in vain and die......
Nan.
- pair exclaims in endless pain...... That one so fine should live.... in vain and die......
Mum
- pair exclaims in endless pain...... That one so fine should live... in vain and die......
Flo.
- pair exclaims in endless pain....... That one so fine should live... in vain and die......
May.
- pair exclaims in endless pain...... That one so fine should live... in vain and die......
Sid
- pair exclaims in endless pain...... That one so fine should live.... in vain and die......
Vic.
- pair exclaims in endless pain...... That one so fine should live... in vain and die......
Sup.
- pair exclaims in endless pain...... That one so fine should live... in vain and die......
ffz
ff
più ffz

Miss W.
.... so young.... die..... so young, die,.......... die,.... die.... so young.............
Ldy. B.
.... so young.... die.... so young, die,.......... die,..... die.... so young.............
Nan.
.... so young.... die..... so young, die,.......... die,..... die.... so young.............
Mum
.... so young.... die.... so young, die,.......... die,..... die..... so young.............
Flo.
.... so young.... die..... so young, die,.......... die,.... die.... so young.............
May.
.... so young.... die.... so young, die,.......... die,.... die.... so young.............
Sid
.... so young.... die.... so young, die,.......... die,.... die.... so young.............
Vic.
.... so young.... die.... so young, die,.......... die,.... die..... so young.............
Sup.
.... so young.... die.... so young, die,.......... die,.... die..... so young.............
fz
dim.
ff
ffz
p
mf dim.

Shop Bell
ppp
rall.
Miss W.
Ldy.B.
Nan.
Mum
Flo.
May.
Sid
Vic.
Sup.
Al - bert?
ALBERT
hesitant (esitando)
What's go-ing on?
pp
Timp.

Much quicker (4 in a bar)
(Molto più mosso)
59
They rise in fury and surround him.
Miss W.
Ldy. B.
Nan.
Mum
Flo.
May.
Sid
Vic.
Sup.
fff
ff
sf
Al-bert!
Where have you come from? Where have you been?

Miss W.
Wreck - ing the whole of our dai - ly rou - tine?
Ldy. B.
Wreck - ing the whole of our dai - ly rou - tine?
Nan
Wreck - ing the whole of our dai - ly rou - tine?
Mum
Wreck - ing the whole of our dai - ly rou - tine?
Flo.
Wreck - ing the whole of our dai - ly rou - tine?
May.
Wreck - ing the whole of our dai - ly rou - tine?
Sid
Wreck - ing the whole of our dai - ly rou - tine?
Vic.
Wreck - ing the whole of our dai - ly rou - tine?
Sup.
Wreck - ing the whole of our dai - ly rou - tine?
ff

60
Very fast, as at the start
(Prestissimo come primo)
Miss W.
Ldy. B.
Nan.
Mum
Flo.
May.
Sid
Vic.
Sup.
pp
Tear - ing the town from its re - gu - lar la - bours, To
Harp
Str.
W.W.
espr.
run up and down and a - round with the neigh - bours — Look - ing for
cresc.
clues, long - ing for news........ In - spect - ing, ac - cept - ing, re -

Miss W.
Ldy. B.
Nan.
Mum
Flo.
- ject - ing re - ports........ That you had been kid - napped or mur - dered or
May.
- ject - ing re - ports........ That you had been kid - napped or mur - dered or
Sid
Vic.
Sup.
- ject - ing re - ports........ That you had been kid - napped or mur - dered or
Miss W.
Ldy. B.
ff
worse For the twen - ty - five sovereigns you had in your purse!
Nan.
ff
worse For the twen - ty - five sovereigns you had in your purse!
Mum
Flo.
ff
worse For the twen - ty - five sovereigns you had in your purse!
May.
ff
worse For the twen - ty - five sovereigns you had in your purse!
Sid
ff
worse For the twen - ty - five sovereigns you had in your purse!
Vic.
Sup.
ff
worse For the twen - ty - five sovereigns you had in your purse!
ff
ff

Much slower (♪= previous 𝅗𝅥.)
(Molto più lento)
61
LADY BILLOWS
ff
"Sor - ry!" "Sor - ry!" He says he's "sor -
ALBERT
p
I'm sor - ry a-bout that!
Much slower (♪= previous 𝅗𝅥.)
(Molto più lento)
61
Str.
ff
Ldy. B.
furious
(furioso)
- ry!" As if a "sor-ry" could re-pay The a-go-ny and wor-ry
62
MISS WORDSWORTH, NANCY & FLORENCE
f
Where ex-act-ly have you
Ldy. B.
He's caused us all.... to - day!......
ALBERT puzzled
Well...
62
ff
sf
f
dim.

Albert is silent. The Vicar steps forward
Miss W.
Nan.
Flo.
been?
MUM balefully
f
Wait...... till I'm a-lone with you!...
MAYOR
f
Tell us that!
SID & VICAR
f
Tell us that!
SUPERINTENDENT
f
Where have you been?
pp
mf
Recit.
to question him.
LADY BILLOWS
Where ex-act-ly did you go?
ALBERT nods YES
no reply
VICAR
You left this house at eight last night?
Recit.
ppp
Piano
pp

MISS WORDSWORTH
Say yes or no!
FLORENCE
Slipped through the streets and out of sight?
nods YES
Alb.
pp
Yes!....
MAYOR
Were you a-lone?
pp
Miss W.
Ac-quaintances?
LADY BILLOWS
Did you remain a-lone for long?
nods NO
nods NO
Alb.
VICAR
You met some friends?
poco più
f

NANCY
f
Oh don't go on!
FLORENCE
Male?
nods YES
nods YES
Alb.
MAYOR
And fe-male?
SUPERINTENDENT
And did you stay with them?
f
LADY BILLOWS
When you left home you took with you twentyfive sovereigns —
Flo.
In gold...
Alb.
Well... Yes!
pp

MUM
How many's left?
nods YES
Alb.
I've twen-ty two
MAYOR
So three have dis-ap-peared all told?
p
MISS WORDSWORTH
Were they stolen from you?
Mum
Did you spend three pounds yourself?
p
Alb.
Yes!
nods NO
nods NO
SUPERINTENDENT
Lost d'you think?
p
p

LADY BILLOWS
At a pub-lic house?
FLORENCE
All that on drink?
nods YES
nods NO
nods YES
Alb.
VICAR
At a shop?
cresc.
NANCY
For good-ness' sake, stop! stop
nods NO
Alb.
MAYOR
How did you spend it?
SID
For good-ness' sake, stop! stop

Nan.
cresc.
pry-ing and poking and probing at him, with your pi-ous old fa-ces de-light-ing in sin!
Sid
cresc.
pry-ing and poking and probing at him, with your pi-ous old fa-ces de-light-ing in sin!
f
slower (più lento)
MISS WORDSWORTH
f
We must per-sist and in-sist on the truth, how-ev-er bad it is
MUM
f
We must per-sist and in-sist on the truth, how-ev-er bad it is
FLORENCE
f
We must per-sist and in-sist on the truth, how-ev-er bad it is
MAYOR
f
We must per-sist and in-sist on the truth, how-ev-er bad it is
VICAR
f
We must per-sist and in-sist on the truth, how-ev-er bad it is
SUPER.
f
We must per-sist and in-sist on the truth, how-ev-er bad it is
slower (più lento)
ff
ff

Miss W.
At once!....
Ldy.B.
Where did that three pounds go? Tell us the truth!.....
Mum
The truth!.......
Flo.
At once!....
May.
The truth!........
Vic.
The truth!........
Sup.
At once!....
f
ff

Albert makes up his mind to confess. He begins quietly and slowly gains confidence.

Alb.
pp sweetly (dolce)
It all........ be - gan........ 'cos I sudden-ly thought it was time I
cresc.
Str. ppp expr.
ought, to try a taste of certain things the Prayer Book ca - ta - logues a - mong its
sins.
sweetly
pp (dolce)
Cu-rio - si-ty killed the cat, they say!
gliss.
(f) dim.
pp
ppp
64
Starting slowly (Cominciando lento)
sempre p
Well, if you like, it was... cu - ri - o - si - ty
made me pinch a bike_ And pe-dal a-way to town last

Alb.
slow accel.
night!... Drink was my first exper-i-ment: I found a pub,.....
ordered some old-and-mild and drank it up. Beer...tasted queer, so my
più
next i-dea was rum: A tum-bler-ful of na-val rum....
with whis-ky and gin to wash it down,.....
65
più f
Be-fore ve-ry long I was pret-ty far gone — reel-ing a-
più f
pp
sim.
sim.

Alb.
- bout, be-ginning to shout, dis-gustingly drunk, a nuisance to ev-eryone...
cresc.
f
dim.
So they threw me out of The Dog and Duck
p
To
MISS WORDSWORTH & LADY BILLOWS pp
Im - pos - si - ble! Drunk and dis -
cresc.
MUM & FLORENCE pp
Im - pos - si - ble! Drunk and dis -
lie in the gut-ter and so - ber up.
MAYOR pp
Im - pos - si - ble! Drunk and dis -
VICAR & SUPERINTENDENT pp
Im - pos - si - ble! Drunk and dis -
pp

66
Miss W.
Ldy. B.
- or - der - ly! Our May - King!
Mum
Flo.
- or - der - ly! Our May - King!
Alb.
mf
Then I
May.
- or - der - ly! Our May - King!
Vlc.
Sup.
- or - der - ly! Our May - King!
66
f heavier (più pesante)
Alb.
staggered a-long to the four-ale bar
f
Of The Horse and Groom, which
sim.
pp
sim.
mf
Alb.
is-n't far:— Start-ed a fight, 'cos they said I was tight,—
p
mf

f sempre
Alb.
But-ted the pub-li-can,— fell on the floor,— and
w.
cresc.
67
MISS WORDSWORTH & LADY BILLOWS
f
Hor-ri-ble! Stop him!
MUM & FLORENCE
f
Hor-ri-ble! Stop him!
with force
(con forza)
Alb.
end - ed up in the gut-ter once more
MAYOR
f
Hor-ri-ble! Stop him!
VICAR & SUPERINTENDENT
f
Hor-ri-ble! Stop him!
67
f
sim.

Miss W.
Ldy. B.
This is re-volting!
Stop! Stop! Stop! Stop!
Mum
Flo.
This is re-volting!
Stop! Stop! Stop! Stop!
Alb.
ff
You wanted the truth........ do you want some
May.
This is re-volting!
Stop! Stop! Stop! Stop!
Vic.
Sup.
This is re-volting!
Stop! Stop! Stop! Stop!
ff
with force
(con forza)
sf Quick (Allegro)
Alb.
more?
Or will that do as a gen-e-ral
sf
fff
p
Alb.
sam-ple of a night that was a night-mare ex-am-ple of drunken-ness,
ff expr.

MUM
But how could you do it? How could you?
Alb.
dirt and worse! You..........
68
.... know what drove me, you....... know how I could.— It was
ff expr.
Wind
Fast (Presto)
= 84)
69
all because you squashed me down and reined me in— Did up my instincts with
Str. pp lightly (leggiero)
safe - ty pins, Kept me wrapped in cot-ton wool, Measured my life by a
pp cresc.

Alb.
twelve-inch rule, Pro - tec - ted me with such de-vo-tion, my on-ly way out..........
pp cresc.
70
MISS WORDSWORTH
ff
Mon - - - - - strous!
LADY BILLOWS
ff
Mon - - - strous!
MUM
ff
Mon - - strous!
FLORENCE
ff
Mon - strous!
Alb.
sf
ff
......was a wild ex - plo - sion!
I've done it
MAYOR
ff
Mon - strous!
VICAR
ff
Mon - strous!
70
f
ff
sim.
sim.

Lady B.
f
Mon - - - - strous!
Mum
f
Mon - - - strous!
Flo.
f
Mon - - strous!
Alb.
now, it was - n't much fun...
f
But
May.
f
Mon - strous!
Vic.
f
Mon - strous!
Sup.
f
Mon - strous!
f
f
mf
NANCY
pp
Good old
Alb.
soon - er or la - ter it had...... to come...
SID
pp
Sid
Good old
Sup.
mf
Mon - - -
p

71
Amiable (very moderate) ♩= 52
(Amabile (molto moderato))
Nan.
Al - bert!
graciously
(grazioso)
Alb.
And I'm more than grateful to you
Sid
Al - bert!
Sup.
- - - strous!....
Amiable (very moderate) ♩= 52
71
(Amabile (molto moderato))
graciously (grazioso)
pp
pp
Str.
pp expr.
MISS WORDSWORTH
f
Wick-ed boy!
MUM & FLORENCE
f
Wick-ed boy!
Alb.
all for kind-ly pro-vi-ding the where-with - al!
MAYOR
f
Preposter - ous!
f
He
VICAR & SUPERINTENDENT
f
Preposter - ous!
f
He

Miss W.
Fan-cy! Turning against his mother! Turning a-gainst his
Mum Flo.
Fan-cy! Turning against his mother! Turning a-gainst his
May.
needs a good thrashing! Young oaf!
Vic. Sup.
needs a good thrashing! Young oaf!
Miss W.
mother!
Mum Flo.
mother!
ALBERT
And now I shall take it ex-treme-ly kind if you'll let.... me get
May.
Young oaf!
Vic. Sup.
Young oaf!
pp

72
LADY BILLOWS furious (furioso)
ff
You will pay, you will pay for your night's ho-li-day! You will pay for your
Alb.
on!
72
Ldy. B.
sins of the flesh. You will creep... to the shade of a pro-fli-gate's grave, a
f
dim.
Ldy. B.
pro-fli-gate's grave, — A dis-grace to your name and your sex!
Good day, your
pp
Alb.
La - dy-ship, please let me get on, for I'm all .... be -

Lady Billows stalks out followed by Miss Wordsworth, Florence, the Superintendent, Vicar and Mayor.
73
dy.B.
ff
Faugh!
Alb.
- hind!
73
MUM
f
I'll never forgive you! – never! – not till my dying day!
Alb.
poco f
That-'ll do, Mum!
dim.
Mum bursts into a fit of sobbing, and goes.
to Sid and Nancy
pp
Alb.
I did'nt lay it on too thick, did I?
D♮
pp
Nancy gives Albert a big kiss.
Albert goes gaily to the window to let up the blinds and sees Emmie, Harry and Cis standing there.
74
Lively
(Vivace)
f SID
Hi! that's my girl!
Bsn. Hrn.
fff
ff
Timp.
Ped.

The children begin their mocking song again.
75
EMMIE CIS & HARRY
ff
Al - bert's Mum
Harp
cresc.
ff
Em.
Cis.
Har.
took a stick, whacked him on the thing - - - - - mi - - - - - jig!
dim.
pp
Albert smiles and _ to their surprise _ beckons them in.
ALBERT p
All right! Come on in! Come on in!
ppp

The kids creep cautiously into the shop. Albert, Sid and Nancy encourage them.

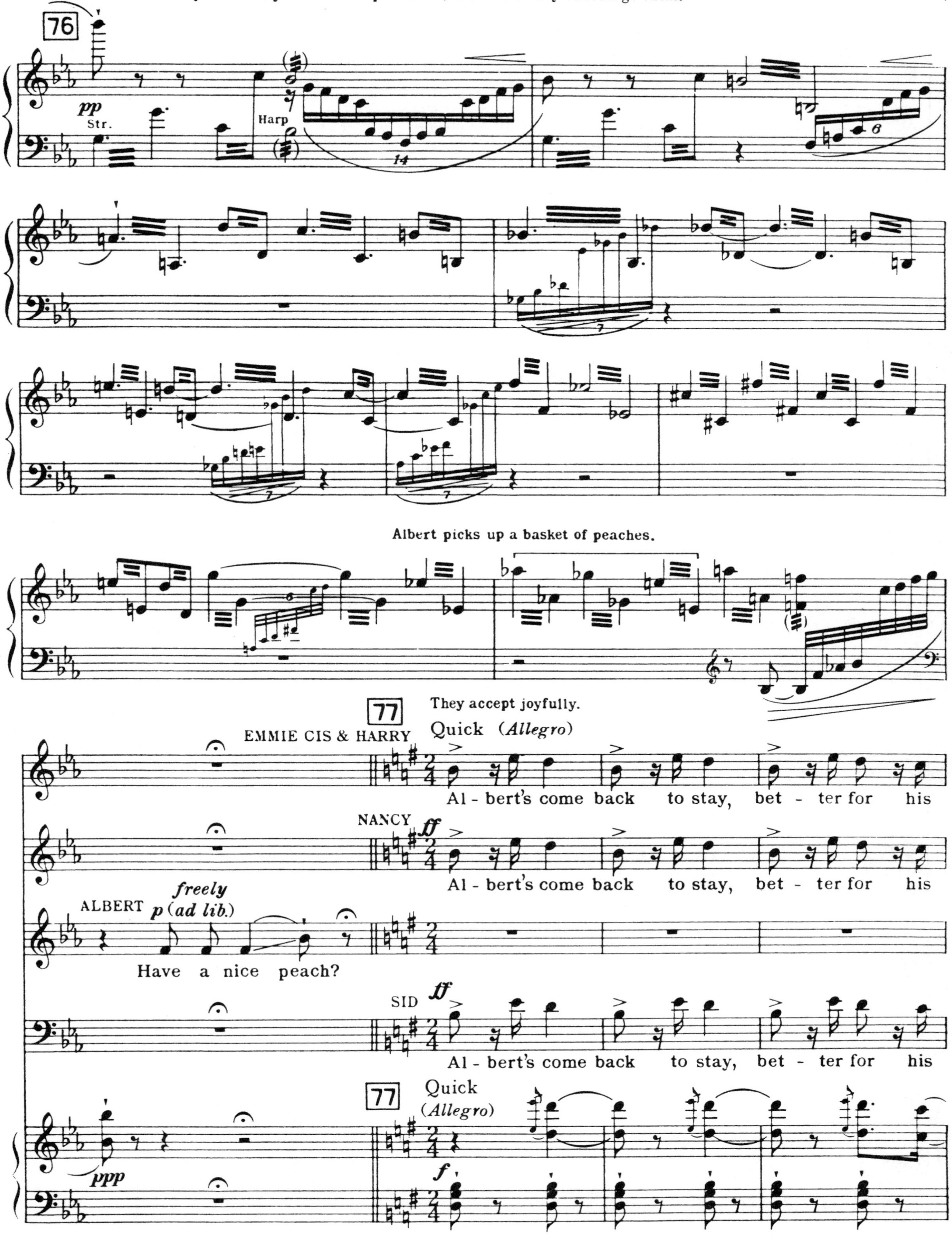

Em.
Cis.
Har.
ho - li-day. Let's all say hip-hip-hoo-ray! Good luck to him
Nan.
ho - li-day. Let's all say hip-hip-hoo-ray! Good luck to him
Alb.
ff
Help your - selves!
Sid
ho - li-day. Let's all say hip-hip-hoo-ray! Good luck to him
Em.
Cis.
Har.
a - ny-way!
ff
Al-bert's come back to stay,
Nan.
a - ny-way!
ff
Al-bert's come back to stay,
Alb.
ff
There's plen-ty.... for ev'-ry-one!
Sid
a - ny-way!
ff
Al-bert's come back to stay,
f
Timp.
f

Em.
Cis.
Har.
bet - ter for his ho - li-day! Let's all say hip-hip-hoo-ray!
Nan.
bet - ter for his ho - li-day! Let's all say hip-hip-hoo-ray!
Alb.
Put some more............ in your poc-kets! It's
Sid.
bet - ter for his ho - li-day! Let's all say hip-hip-hoo-ray!
78
Em.
Cis.
Har.
Good luck to him a - ny-way!
Nan.
Good luck to him a - ny-way!
Alb.
nice.. to be home a-gain.
Sid picks up the wreath of orange blossom.
Sid.
Good luck to him a - ny-way! Hi! You'd bet - ter frame this!
78
Timp.

Sid throws the wreath to Albert, who catches it and skims it out over the heads of the audience.
ALBERT
Chuck it o-ver!
They all wave goodbye to the wreath, laughing.
EMMIE, CIS & HARRY
Jol - ly good rid - dance!
NANCY
Jol - ly good rid - dance!
ALBERT
Jol - ly good rid - dance!
SID
Jol - ly good rid - dance!
CURTAIN

End of Opera

Reproduced and printed by Halstan & Co. Ltd., Amersham, Bucks., England

DATE DUE
